THE YELLOW BOOK

The Yellow Book is the most famous of the literary magazines of the 1890s, summing up the mood of those years, when aesthetics became a subject for fierce debate, satirized by *Punch* and by W.S. Gilbert, and as fiercely defended by the artists and writers who formed the new movement. *The Yellow Book*, in its brief three years of existence, came in for more than its fair share of denunciation and derision, particularly for its illustrations by Aubrey Beardsley. Fraser Harrison's selection allows us to find out what all the fuss was about, and he contributes an introduction on the history of the magazine and its social and artistic context. His essay and the selection of contents, by authors and artists who are now deservedly famous, show that *The Yellow Book* was not merely a *succès de scandale*, but still has much to offer us today.

The Yellow Book

An Illustrated Quarterly

THE YELLOW BOOK

An anthology selected and introduced
by Fraser Harrison

THE BOYDELL PRESS

Introduction and selection © Fraser Harrison 1914

First published in this series 1982
by The Boydell Press
an imprint of Boydell Brewer Ltd
PO Box 9, Woodbridge, Suffolk, IP12 3DF

British Library Cataloguing in Publication Data

The Yellow book.
  1. English literature—19th century
  2. Art, English—19th century
  I. Harrison, Fraser
  820.8'008   PR1145

ISBN 0 85115 207 4

Printed in Great Britain by
Nene Litho, Wellingborough, Northants

Contents

Literature

Pictures

Introduction

"My dear boy, do not say nice false things about The Yellow Book. I bought it at the station, but before I had cut all the pages I threw it out of the carriage window. Suddenly the train stopped and the guard, opening the door, said 'Mr. Wilde, you have dropped The Yellow Book.' What was to be done? In the hansom, with the subtlety of a poet, I cunningly hid it under the cushions and paid my fare . . . When came a loud knocking at the front door, and the cabby appearing, said 'Mr. Wilde, you have forgotten The Yellow Book.'" (Oscar Wilde to Charles Ricketts)

I

The idea of *The Yellow Book* was initially canvassed by Aubrey Beardsley and Henry Harland, both of whom in January 1894 were looking for new opportunities to exploit their own respective talents. They approached John Lane and suggested that he launch a magazine that was to be "representative of the most cultural work which was then being done in England . . . with no hall-mark except that of excellence and no prejudice against anything except dullness and incapacity". Lane eagerly encouraged them and agreed with his partner Elkin Mathews to finance and publish their brain-child.

By March a characteristically brash announcement was issued, decorated by a Beardsley drawing which depicted an exotically behatted lady casting a hungry eye over a bin of books outside a bookshop; the bookseller was clad, appropriately, in Pierrot costume.

'The aim . . . of *The Yellow Book* is to depart as far as may be from the bad old traditions of periodical literature, and to provide an Illustrated Magazine which shall be beautiful as a piece of bookmaking, modern and distinguished in its letter-press and its pictures, and withal popular in the better sense of the word. It is felt that such a Magazine, at present, is conspicuous by its absence . . .

. . . And while *The Yellow Book* will seek always to preserve a delicate, decorous, and reticent mien and conduct, it will at the same time have the courage of its modernness, and not tremble at the frown of Mrs Grundy.

Altogether, it is expected that *The Yellow Book* will prove the most interesting, unusual, and important publication of its kind that has ever been undertaken. It will be charming, it will be daring, it will be distinguished. It will be a *book*—a book to be read, and placed upon one's shelves, and read again; a book in form, a book in substance; a book beautiful to see and convenient to handle; a book with style, a book with finish; a book that every book-lover will love at first sight; a book that will make book-lovers of many who are now indifferent to books.

The Yellow Book will contain no advertisements other than publishers' lists.'

In the event, some of the names listed in this announcement never appeared in the magazine, but as Arthur Waugh, Evelyn's father, later wrote in his autobiography: "There was no sort of hint that *The Yellow Book* was to be the oriflamme of decadence; indeed, if any such suggestion had been made to its publisher, he would have become inarticulate on the spot. For Lane was dreadfully afraid of offending the proprieties, or indeed causing any annoyance to any person of importance . . . So the table of contents for the first number of *The Yellow Book* was an ingenious study in compromise; there was in point of fact no real Yellow Book atmosphere; the sly new-comer intended to be all things to all men."

John Lane had already established himself as one of London's leading *avant-garde* publishers. He had a shrewd eye for talent, particularly talent that was potentially fashionable, and he had suggested Beardsley to Wilde when in 1893 they were looking for an artist to illustrate Wilde's play, *Salomé*. Beardsley (1872–98) was then a mere twenty years old, but his drawings for Dent's edition of Mallory's *Morte D'Arthur* had already won him a measure of fame.

He and Wilde enjoyed an uneasy friendship. Beardsley had been piqued when Wilde, not surprisingly, chose Alfred Douglas in favour of him to translate *Salomé* from its original French, but he took typical revenge by caricaturing his benefactor no less than four times in his *Salomé* drawings. Wilde appears at first to have been fascinated by Lane's consumptive protégé: "He has a face like a silver hatchet adorned by grass green hair." Later he dismissed him as not flesh and blood, but rather "a monstrous orchid", and claimed to have invented him. He disliked Beardsley's illustrations for his play: "They are too Japanese, while my play is Byzantine . . . They are like the scribbles a precocious boy makes on the margins of his copybooks." But the drawings made the play famous, and Beardsley fashionable.

Association with the most famous playwright of the day—*A Woman of No Importance* was then running at The Haymarket—had put Beardsley in the limelight, but when he, Lane and Harland laid their plans for *The Yellow Book* he insisted that Wilde should never be a contributor. Neither of his colleagues demurred.

In the astonishingly brief period of four months this team succeeded in putting together the first volume, which included stories by Henry James and Ella D'Arcy, poems by Richard Le Gallienne, Arthur Symons and John Davidson, articles by Max Beerbohm and George Saintsbury and illustrations by Frederic Leighton, Walter Sickert, Will Rothenstein, Laurence Houseman, and of course Beardsley himself.

Publication day was 15 April 1894. London suddenly turned yellow, and naturally the boldest display was at the Bodley Head's Vigo Street office where the little bow window was filled with copies "creating such a mighty glow of yellow at the far end of Vigo Street that one might have been forgiven for imagining for a moment that some awful portent had happened, and that the sun had risen in the West!"★

The phenomenon was not, however, kindly received. *The National Observer* delivered a broadside of insults: "bizarre, eccentric, uncomfortably heavy to the hand . . . the audacious vulgarity and the laborious inelegance of the cover . . . a misarrangement in orpiment . . . nonsensical and hysterical matter". *The Times* condemned it as "a combination of English rowdiness with French lubricity." "The cover" (by Beardsley) it said "may be intended to attract by its very repulsiveness and insolence." *Punch* pithily summed up its attitude in the epigram "uncleanliness is next to Bodliness". Most reviewers echoed this tone of outrage and disgust, but *The Westminster* hit the highest note of indignation. Having dismissed Max Beerbohm's essay "A Defence of Cosmetics" as pernicious nonsense, it turned its attention to one of Beardsley's drawings and declared: "We do not know that anything would meet the case except a short act of Parliament to make this kind of thing illegal."

With publicity like this the magazine could not fail. A second printing was rushed out during that week, and a third was on the press by the weekend. The critics had concentrated their fire on Beerbohm, who remarked later, "as far as anyone in literature is lynched, I was", on Symons, whose poem "Stella Maris" celebrated a night spent with a prostitute, and on Beardsley. All three were gratified, and Beardsley positively revelled in his notoriety. *Punch*

★John Lane and the Nineties, *J. Lewis May, 1936*.

wittily   dubbed   him   "Weirdsley   Daubery",   "Awfully
Weirdly" and "Daubaway Weirdsley"; Beerbohm became "Max
Mereboom" and their work was supposed to issue from "The Bogey
Head".

Other contributors were less amused. Sir Frederic Leighton, the
then President of the Royal Academy, whose drawing of two grey
figures, muffled in drapery, posing meditatively against a grey
background, had received pride of place among the illustrations,
provoked *The Times*'s commiseration: "Leighton . . . finds himself
cheek by jowl with such advanced and riotous representatives of the
new art as Mr Aubrey Beardsley and Mr Walter Sickert." He
immediately informed Lane that he had been reprimanded by his
friends for embarrassing serious art, and thus *The Yellow Book* lost a
valuable contributor.

Henry James too found the company he was obliged to keep
unattractive. "I haven't sent you *The Yellow Book* on purpose," he
wrote to his brother William, "and indeed I have been weeks and
weeks receiving a copy of it myself. I say on purpose because
although my little tale . . . appears to have had, for a thing of mine,
an unusual success, I hate too much the horrid aspect and company of
the whole publication. And yet I am to be intimately, conspicuously
associated with the second number. It is for gold and to oblige the
worshipful Harland." In fact he obliged the worshipful Harland with
three stories and an essay in all.

The next three volumes★ were published with equal *éclat*; the press
remained hostile but grew less vituperative.

This carefree era came, however, to an abrupt end on 5 April 1895.
Oscar Wilde, following the failure of his libel case against the
Marquess of Queensberry, Lord Alfred Douglas's father, was
arrested on morals charges at the Cadogan Hotel, and removed in a
four-wheeler to Bow Street police station. On his way out, Wilde,
according to the press, "grasped his suede gloves in one hand and
seized his stick with the other. Then he picked up from the table a
copy of *The Yellow Book* which he placed in security under his left
arm."

John Lane was on his way to America at the time, but when his
ship docked he was handed a newspaper with the headline: "Arrest
of Oscar Wilde, *Yellow Book* under his arm." Meanwhile crowds had
gathered at Vigo Street and stoned the bow window under the sign
of The Bodley Head. Lane had more than one reason to be nervous,
for Wilde, a few months previously, had enjoyed a minor affair with

★*Between the second and third volumes Lane and Elkin Mathews separated. Lane took with
him the Bodley Head imprint, a great many authors, and* The Yellow Book.

one of the Bodley Head clerks, Edward Shelley. The poet had flattered the boy, encouraged his literary aspirations, and then dropped him. Shelley had fallen into disconsolate despair, and had been sacked. Lane cabled Frederick Chapman, his assistant, instructing him to withdraw all Wilde's publications. He in his turn received cables from London. Goaded by Mrs Humphrey Ward, several of his authors expressed their horror and demanded Beardsley's dismissal. William Watson summed up the situation: WITHDRAW ALL BEARDSLEY'S DESIGNS OR I WITHDRAW MY BOOKS. The fifth volume was at the printers, but after a day or two of hesitation, Chapman recalled it and expunged all trace of Beardsley. Two weeks late, on 30 April 1895, the new, emasculated version was published. "It turned grey overnight," E. F. Benson remarked.

Apart from the fact that at the time Beardsley and Wilde were scarcely on speaking terms, the extraordinary irony was that the fatal volume under Wilde's arm was not *The Yellow Book* at all, but a French novel, *Aphrodite* by Pierre Louys, which happened to be bound in yellow. Beardsley may have been foppish and affected but there is no evidence that he was a homosexual. Indeed, in Stanley Weintraub's excellent biography there is no suggestion that he had a single romantic experience, far less a sexual one. But in the mind of Mrs Humphrey Ward and the like, Wilde and Beardsley were indistinguishable. She presumably saw Beardsley as a threat to common decency and from her point of view she was perhaps right, for during the remaining three years of his life, his work, free of Lane's vigilant restraint, became increasingly erotic.

Lane had always sailed close to the moral wind, but he had a genius for calculating just how far he could go without alienating respectable opinion. The magazine had been his most *risqué* venture, and one of his most successful, but, through no fault of his and despite his never-failing caution, it blew up in his face. He said later that the Wilde scandal "killed *The Yellow Book*, and it nearly killed me!" In point of fact they both survived: he to the age of seventy, *The Yellow Book* for nine more volumes. These nine "grey" volumes, although often derided, contain the bulk of the best contributions. Beardsley was certainly irreplaceable,★ but, with the significant exception of Symons, none of the contributors to the first four volumes felt obliged, as a matter of principle, to leave with him or because of him. James, Beerbohm, Grahame and many of the other original contributors remained loyal, and they were joined, in succeeding volumes by, among others, Gissing, Wells, Bennett, Buchan, Baron

★*Lane himself took over the supervision of the illustrations and was occasionally helped by Laurence Housman.*

Corvo and Yeats. Admittedly its demeanour after Beardsley's departure was more subdued, but for two more years it proceeded to flourish and maintain its standards.

Beardsley, after a period of drunken melancholy, collaborated with Arthur Symons and launched another magazine, *The Savoy*, which in its turn became a *succés de scandale*, to its editors' delight. It was published by Leonard Smithers, who could not have been more different to Lane. Part-pornographer, part-publisher, he prided himself on publishing what other, more conventional publishers dared not touch. Wilde described him in a letter to Reggie Turner: "He loves first editions, especially of women: little girls are his passion. He is the most learned erotomaniac in Europe. He is also a delightful companion, and a dear fellow, very kind to me."

Wilde also called him "the owner of Beardsley". With Smithers' encouragement, Beardsley went on to produce more brilliant work, and as his health grew worse his preoccupation with the erotic developed into an obsession, culminating in his unequivocally pornographic drawings for Smithers' edition of *Lysistrata*.

The series of coincidences linking Beardsley with Wilde was not quite complete, for it was Smithers who published Wilde's only book after his imprisonment, *The Ballad of Reading Gaol*, in February 1898. Beardsley died a month later at the age of twenty-five years, seven months.

Shortly after Beardsley's death Wilde wrote to Smithers: "I was greatly shocked to read of poor Aubrey's death. Superbly premature as the flowering of his genius was, still he had immense development, and had not sounded his last stop. There were great possibilities always in the cavern of his soul, and there is something macabre and tragic in the fact that one who added another terror to life should have died at the age of a flower."

On 30 November 1900 Wilde himself died, aged fifty-seven. Five years later Henry Harland also died, of tuberculosis, aged forty-four.

Ever since those first, infuriated reviews, *The Yellow Book* has taken its place, along with Wilde, in the mythology of the nineties; it seems even now to represent some quintessential characteristic of its times. In 1914 Wyndham Lewis wrote in his manifesto for the magazine *Blast*, "The spirit and purpose of the Arts and Literature of Today are expressed in BLAST. No periodical since the famous *Yellow Book* has so comprehended the artistic movement of its decade. The artistic spirit of the Eighteen Nineties was *The Yellow Book*." It was a fitting obituary, and, like all obituaries, it was a little less than disinterested, and a little kinder than it was accurate.

II

In March 1894, after sixty-one years in the House of Commons, Gladstone, the Prime Minister, resigned. It was during the same month that John Lane and Elkin Mathews, with notable panache, announced the imminent publication of *The Yellow Book*.

The coincidence, no doubt, lacks profound significance, but to *The Yellow Book* devotee there is something revealing about this little conjunction of events. It would be fanciful to imagine that simply because the numerical chronology of a century was nearing its end, history would dutifully take note of the calendar and throw herself into a frenzy of termination. And yet one of the oddest characteristics of the 1890s is that they did indeed witness an eerily disproportionate number of beginnings and ends, births and deaths. This union of calendar and history is unnerving and lends foundation to the over-exploited phrase *fin de siécle*. The question which exercises the devotee is, however, to whose age did *The Yellow Book* truly belong: Gladstone's or Asquith's? Was it the last, bizarre throw of moribund Victorian sensibility, or was it instead a harbinger, in Victorian disguise, of what was to come?

A curious feature of critical and biographical writing devoted to the arts of the period is that the surrounding historical landscape is often obscured, even obliterated. This is particularly true of accounts of Wilde, the protagonists in his melodrama, and his literary colleagues. Their era is depicted as having its existence in some theatrical limbo, peopled exclusively by witty and/or tragic aesthetes and fulminating representatives of the bourgeoisie. Wilde himself is generally seen as the willing victim of his own noble folly, while his judge and prosecutor, together with a vindictive public, are seen as ogres of hypocrisy and cant. Though the stuff of legend, such an interpretation is hardly the truth of the matter.

The Yellow Book has suffered a similar fate: isolating it from its literary and publishing context, critics have tended to regard it solely as a product of the decadent movement. Hesketh Pearson, in his celebrated biography of Oscar Wilde, shares his hero's opinion, and curtly condemns it: "This quarterly publication . . . has in some curious way become associated with the forward movement of the nineties in arts and letters. It is supposed to have expressed the daring and rebellious spirit of youth, straining at the leash of Victorian respectability. It did nothing of the sort. It favoured no movement, it displayed no tendency . . . The only startling note was provided by Beardsley, who, however, was only permitted to alarm the readers for four numbers." In other words, *The Yellow Book* is contemptible because it is not what it pretended to be; it was a piece of low fraud which fortunately has been detected and exposed.

The other accusation most commonly thrown at the magazine's head is that after the Wilde debacle and Beardsley's dismissal it suffered a near-fatal stroke from which it recovered only to linger on its death-bed, frail and tame, until, nine volumes later, it finally expired, unmourned by readers and editorial staff alike.

Both this criticism, and the suggestion that the magazine was a manifesto of a movement whose members never signed it, stem from the assumption that *The Yellow Book* is in the mainstream of decadent writing. Since this is by no means the case, it is hardly surprising that many people have found it a disappointing example of a breed to which it never belonged. Rebutting these attacks does not necessarily involve the dramatic unmasking of hitherto unrecognized nuggets of literary gold; it does, however, involve placing the magazine in a new context, a context prescribed by the social conditions in which it flourished and foundered.

One of the functions of this present collection is to provide the next best thing to the original; a complete set of the magazine is now both difficult to find and expensive to buy. This collection is designed not only to resemble the original in its physical appearance but also to furnish a representative cross-section of the original contents. When compiling a volume of this kind it is perhaps tempting to gut the wreck, pick out the choicest gems and entitle the booty "The Best of . . ." While this method reassures the customer that the goods are of the first water, it does not necessarily do justice to or accurately reflect the original, particularly if the reputation of the magazine in question was founded not on a few random contributions by celebrated writers, but on an aura emanated by the magazine as a whole. In the case of *The Yellow Book*, conveying a sense of authenticity cannot be simply a case of running one's eye down the contents pages of the thirteen volumes and putting together a short list of names that would carry weight with a contemporary reader—although this would not be difficult. Nor can it be a question of choosing those pieces which seem to exude most vigorously the spirit of *fin de siecle*. Either method would distort. The pieces in this collection have been selected purely on the principle of representing those themes which seem to dominate, and those writers who dominate either by the power of individual stories or poems or by the frequency of their contributions.

This collection is intended to be a composite facsimile. The design of the jacket is taken from Volume IV, and is by Beardsley whose covers were incomparably better than anything used in the later volumes. He only designed one back cover which was used in the first four volumes and, by an ironical oversight, in the fifth, although every effort was made to excise his work after his dismissal. He designed two spines: one for Volumes I and II, the other for Volumes III and IV, which was also, presumably inadvertently, used for Volume V. He had prepared a number of drawings for Volume V, which, unfortunately for the magazine but fortunately for him, he was able to use subsequently in *The Savoy*. The magazine's design and lay-out which he inaugurated remained unchanged after his departure and the later covers were more or less pale imitations of his style. The illustrations, which varied between thirteen and twenty-six in any one volume, were scattered seemingly at random between the stories and poems, although some attempt was made to place them more pointedly while Beardsley was Art Editor: the conjunction of Arthur Symons' poem "Stella Maris" and Beardsley's own "Night Piece" can hardly have been a coincidence. Sheets of tissue paper were inserted to protect the illustrations, a refinement, due to modern manufacturing costs, impossible to reproduce.

Each volume terminated in a series of publishers' advertisements and John Lane's own Belles Lettres list, which included the back numbers of *The Yellow Book*. The Lane list demonstrates how vigorously he led the field during this period, for most of the famous nineties' names are represented. A number of Wilde's books were published by The Bodley Head, mostly in limited editions: *The Sphinx* (a poem), *The Story of Mr WH*, both decorated by Charles Ricketts, *Lady Windermere's Fan, A Woman of No Importance, The Duchess of Padua*, all with bindings designed by Charles Shannon, and *Salomé*, with illustrations and cover design by Beardsley. All these were removed immediately after Wilde's arrest from the advertisement to be carried in Volume V and never reappeared. Although Beardsley himself was dismissed, it was evidently deemed acceptable that his *Story of Venus and Tanhauser* should continue to be advertised. *Salomé* shared the fate of Wilde's other work. The advertisements for Harland's *Grey Roses* and Ella D'Arcy's *Monochromes* gives an indication, even allowing for the highly selective bias with which all publishers compose such advertisements, of their considerable critical reputation at the time. The Belles Lettres list also contains the work of most of *The Yellow Book*'s regular contributors.

The length of the volumes varied between 256 pages (Volume IX) and 406 (Volume VIII); of the literary contents anything between a third and a half consisted of poetry, but, since none of the poems was longer than seven pages (John Davidson's *The Ballad of a Nun*), and most barely occupied a page, the prose predominated.

Fearing a reputation for excessive flippancy, and keen to demonstrate that their magazine had its serious side, Lane and Harland solicited a number of essays on literary and historical topics, designed to indicate an underlying spirit of editorial dignity and responsibility. Each volume contained one essay of this kind; some contained two or three. On the whole they are earnest, worthy, and dull. Max Beerbohm's essays "1880", "A Note on George the Fourth" and "A Defence of Cosmetics" are exceptions.

Lane felt it would be an amusing and stimulating idea to include in each volume an article examining the virtues and failings of the previous volume. Consequently the distinguished and, presumably, incorruptible man of letters and art critic Philip G. Hamerton was invited to pronounce mercilessly on Volume I. His critique duly appeared in Volume II. It has the embarrassing air of a fix, which it certainly was not, for he found next to nothing to condemn and much to commend. Apart from "regretting" the publication of "Stella Maris" and asking plaintively, "why should poetic art be employed to celebrate common fornication?", he was full of praise, going so far as to defend Beerbohm and to declare Beardsley "a man of genius", an extravagance which only earned him and the magazine fresh outcries from other critics. The experiment was not repeated.

This strain of complacent masochism was revived by Harland himself in three pseudonymous letters he wrote to the editor from "The Yellow Dwarf". Purporting to be the scourge of pretension, and of The Yellow Book's pretensions in particular, the Dwarf jauntily surveyed the literary scene with what is supposed to be a sharp, unblinkered eye. While continually threatening to castigate the magazine for its mildest fault, Harland in fact used the letters as a thin excuse for lavishing shameless praise on his own contributors. Impudent and arch in tone, they presumably provide an insight of sorts into his character, although they can hardly have done the magazine a service.

Not satisfied with being both editor and critic, Harland was also the magazine's most prolific contributor. Every volume contained at least one story by him under his own name, and, apart from The Yellow Dwarf, he used two other pseudonyms. His behaviour was not however as vainglorious as it might appear today, for although none of his work is now in print, he was then a novelist of some standing and considerable experience. He was also by no means the only editor who consistently printed his own work: Beardsley and Symons created The Savoy specifically in order to provide an alternative outlet to *The Yellow Book* for their own material.

As a young man in New York, Harland had written a number of novels about the Jewish community, which had been highly praised, and had adopted a suitably Jewish-sounding pseudonym: Sydney Luska. When later he came to Europe, fell under the spell of French writers and began to write in their vein, he resumed his real name. But throughout his life his origins and background were shrouded in exotic mystery: he laid claim, in no less an organ than the *Dictionary of National Biography*, to St Petersburg as his birthplace, and to an aristocratic ancestry. Rumour, no doubt assiduously fed by him, had it that he was the natural son of the Emperor Franz Joseph. He was in fact born in New York, the son of a businessman.

These colourful eccentricities seem only to have endeared him to his contemporaries, for by the time he was editor of *The Yellow Book* he was a respected and popular literary figure. Beerbohm described him as "the most joyous of men and the most generous of critics." He appears to have been indefatigable in his efforts to help other writers, particularly unknown or young ones; he was devoted to his work—"Art, with him," said Le Gallienne, "was a life and death matter"; and no one can have campaigned as hard or as imaginatively to promote the short story as an acceptable and significant literary form. De Maupassant, Daudet and Merimée were his masters, and *The Yellow Book* was both his tribute to them, and his attempt to establish their genre on an equal footing in England.

Next to Harland, Ella D'Arcy was *The Yellow Book*'s most prolific contributor, with eleven stories to her name. She also acted as Harland's part-time editorial assistant and it is perhaps thanks to her that women writers provided such a substantial proportion of the magazine, for more than a third of the poems and stories are written by them.

Richard Le Gallienne, who was also a close friend of Harland, had more titles to his name than any other contributor—three poems, fifteen prose fancies and one story—but they are all short, and do not amount to anything like the number of words contributed by Harland, Ella D'Arcy or Henry James, whose three stories were very long, (the longest, "The Coxon Fund", is seventy pages). The prose fancy, or prose poem as Wilde called it, was a very typical nineties' form, and of all *The Yellow Book* pieces Le Gallienne's come closest to sounding the authentic decadent note. His pose of poet incarcerated in a grubby, vulgar world, whose infinitely sensitive soul yearns for transcendent mystery and beauty, gives him the opportunity both to mock and indulge the more effete absurdities of decadence. "Variations upon Whitebait" (Volume VIII) is a typical example:

The author and his girl-friend are dining in a restaurant; she asks him how the whitebait they are eating "get their beautiful little silver water-proofs".

"Electric Light of the World," I said, "it is like this. While they are still quite young and full of dreams, their mother takes them out in picnic parties of a billion or so at a time to where the spring moon is shining, scattering silver from its purse of pearl far over the wide waters, silver, silver, for every little whitebait that cares to swim and pick it up. The mother, who has a contract with some such big restaurateur as ours here, chooses a convenient area of moonlight, and then at a given sign they all turn over on their sides, and bask and bask in the rays, little fin pressed lovingly against little fin—for this is the happiest in the young whitebait's life: it is at these silvering parties that matches are made and future consignments of whitebait arranged for. Well, night after night, they thus lie in the moonlight, first on one side then on the other, till by degrees, tiny scale by scale, they have become completely lunar plated. Ah! how sad they are when the end of that happy time has come."

A number of other writers and poets contributed regularly to the magazine: Max Beerbohm, Hubert Crackanthorpe, William Watson, H. B. Marriot Watson, his wife Rosamund Marriot Watson, Evelyn Sharp, Olive Custance and Henry James. Among the artists who contributed regularly were Walter Sickert, Will Rothenstein, Charles Condor, Patten Wilson and Wilson Steer. Beardsley, during his short tenure of office, besides designing covers and title pages, drew sixteen illustrations for the magazine, two under the pseudonyms Philip Broughton and Albert Foschter for Volume III, which to his glee, were warmly praised.

Most of these writers and artists are represented in this collection.*

III

Among so many contributors of differing backgrounds and ages, it would be surprising if any one theme or preoccupation was found to be held in common. The identity of woman, and, more specifically, her sexuality were, however, issues that dominated, either overtly or by implication, an enormous number of *Yellow Book*

---

*Henry James must seem the most glaring omission. However, his three stories, by Yellow Book standards, are long; including one of them would have meant omitting two or three by other, lesser known or forgotten writers who are seldom, if ever, reprinted.

stories. This can hardly have been the result of editorial policy, nor was it the result of Harland's commissioning so many women writers, for these themes obsessed both the men and the women alike, and neither group displays more or less radicalism or conservatism than the other.

"Marcel: An Hotel Child" by Lena Milman (Volume XII), provides an example of a story in which female sexuality was, as it were, the unconscious theme underlying the apparent one.

The narrator, an English gentleman on his travels, makes the acquaintance in Venice of a small boy, one Marcel Van Lunn, son of Mrs Van Lunn, a wealthy American widow. Mama and her son, it transpires, eke out an arid if expensive existence by traipsing round the pleasure haunts of Europe at the whim of Mama's lover, who is cryptically referred to as "Monsieur". Mama, not unreasonably, is keener on spending her time with "Monsieur" than with her lonely but forbearing son. The more she neglects the boy, the more he turns to the Catholic Church, focussing his unrequited filial affection on the Virgin Mary. His real mother, meanwhile, is gadding about the canals, making an exhibition of herself with her lover.

The narrator is informed by a resident gossip that Mrs Van Lunn has put herself beyond the social pale, for "Monsieur Casimir Portel is neither her first, nor likely to be her last 'travelling companion'." "I cared not at all," the narrator reports, "as far as Mrs Van Lunn was concerned, but, as I listened to the sordid story, I saw again the pathetic profile of Marcel, and felt gloomily conscious of my impotence to avert the misery which I saw threaten." He has, as it turns out, good grounds for these despondent ruminations for, some six months later, he once again runs into the Van Lunns only to discover that his young friend has caught a mysterious fever. The boy languishes in bed for some days—he lacks "recuperative force"—and then, to everyone's relief, appears to be on the mend. Mrs Van Lunn immediately departs for Palermo, claiming to have been called there on urgent business, although the narrator makes it clear that he, for one, is not fooled by this trumpery and knows lechery when he sees it.

On his mother's disappearance Marcel suffers a relapse. He overhears some people in the next door room accuse her of neglecting him, staggers in, passionately defends her and expires shortly after with the word "mother" on his lips. "Was it," the narrator muses, "a vision of the blue-robed, star-crowned Madonna that he had so greeted, or one of Mrs Van Lunn, in her *Doucet* travelling suit, as he had seen her last, as he had so longed to see her again?"

Six months later the narrator reads an announcement of Mrs Van

Lunn's marriage to M. Portel. "So Mrs Van Lunn was *rangée*. The obstacle had been removed!"

Mrs Van Lunn's neglect of her child, though reprehensible, hardly merits the cruel punishment it receives. Her real crime is, of course, her shameless devotion, in the face of society's open disapproval, to a man not her husband; the fact that both of them are foreigners with funny names only makes matters worse. Although she presumably loved her M. Portel, and may even have lived happily and respectably ever after with him, her story is described as squalid, and so it was, in 1894. She chose to flout a sacred convention and, consequently, she was obliged to endure not merely the indignity of a sullied reputation but also the death of her son. Not that his decease is depicted as a direct, moral effect of her misbehaviour, but it is unequivocally seen as a well-deserved repercussion.

Fatal repercussions of this kind occur again and again in *Yellow Book* stories when women attempt to take the initiative, particularly in marriage, or attempt to assert themselves emotionally.

In, for instance, "The Elsingfords" by Henry Harland, a dowdy and absurd woman, notorious for the tedium of her tea-parties, succeeds in marrying, much to the astonishment and amusement of his friends, a celebrated artist. After the wedding she insists on their living in America, her homeland, and reveals that she hates England and the English. When, four years later, they return to Europe, she refuses to live in London and they take up residence in Paris. He complains the climate is bad for his health; she derides what she calls his hypochondria: "Be a man! Get up and go out. Don't stick at home molly-coddling yourself like an old woman." Although the husband rises heroically to the challenge, soon enough he contracts a sinister cough and is confined to his bed. A doctor advises him to leave immediately for Egypt if he wants to save his life. His wife is prostrated: "If I had dreamed—if I had dreamed that it was anything serious."

Death, in this case, is cheated of its victim, but Harland makes it clear that when wives, particularly feather-headed wives manifestly inferior to their husbands, start to dictate terms in a marriage the consequences can only be regrettable, if not fatal.

Ella D'Arcy's bleakly entitled story "A Marriage", (Volume XI), included in this collection, contains the same elements, although they are painted in far more macabre colours. The hero of her story, against the advice of his friend, the narrator, decides to do the decent thing by his mistress, even though this involves a drop in class status. Prior to the marriage the girl is thought by her lover to be a model of domestic modesty, but, once married, this paragon transforms herself into a virago of pretension and intolerance. The scales fall from the husband's eyes, and as his wife glides implacably up the ladder of social advancement, he is left behind to brood bitterly on his folly—and the folly of marriage generally. Sure enough, he too contracts the sinister cough, and dies.

Neither neglect nor carelessness killed this husband; the poor fellow simply succumbed to his wife's superior psychological strength. She was invincibly selfish and he was unequal to the struggle.

Netta Syrett's "Thy Heart's Desire" (Volume II) seems to suggest that even the contemplation of infidelity on the part of a wife is sufficient to loosen her husband's frail grasp on life. The couple in this case are living in a tent in a remote corner of India; the wife finds their isolation hard to bear, she is not cut out for colonial exile and she misses her books and friends. Her husband, a bluff, good-hearted chap, but "not much of a reader", positively relishes their rugged existence and fails to appreciate how much she is suffering. Into their camp rides a dashing friend of the husband, bearing a packing case full of books; friend and wife experience mutual attraction; he makes a pass, but, after a moment's passionate hesitation, her better self triumphs and she resists temptation. The damage is, however, done; within two days her husband is dead. No romantic cough for him, he is bluntly declared defunct.

Perhaps the most revealing example of death at the hands of insurgent femininity is H. B. Marriot Watson's "The Dead Wall" (Volume VI) which is also included in this collection. The wife in this instance does not obliquely provoke her husband's death, she actually drives him to suicide.

The very quality of melodrama inherent in so many of these stories is an indication of the terror that the possibility of female liberation, in the modern sense of heightened consciousness, must have struck in the hearts of husbands and wives alike during this decade. The middle-class wife who found her repressed situation irksome must have also feared the consequences of her liberty, regardless of whether or not her husband was sympathetic. She not only had to bear and combat the prejudice, hostility and ridicule of society at large, she not only had to put into perspective the propaganda of a century, but she also had to come to terms with the prospect of disastrously upsetting the balance of her domestic life. It is at the centre of this dilemma that *The Yellow Book* stories stand. Few of them unequivocally champion either the male or female cause, but all of them are concerned with accounting the price that must be paid when a woman interferes with the marital *status quo*.

Women, no less than men, must have feared, however unconsciously, that their right to assert themselves could only be obtained
by sacrificing their husband's manliness. By challenging the concept
of male supremacy they automatically question their husband's
virility.

Convention, to say nothing of John Lane, prevented *The Yellow
Book* writers describing their characters' sex lives, but most of the
stories, particularly Marriot Watson's, are fraught with sexual tension. The narrator in "Marcel", for instance, says he feels "impo-
tent" in the face of Mrs Van Lunn's behaviour. Mrs Elsingford in
Harland's story is constantly urging her husband to "be a man". The
husband in "The Dead Wall" when threatening suicide in front of his
wife, "handles" a revolver and "cocks it" to lend conviction to his
threat; she reduces him, however, to such a pitch of emasculation
that instead of using the revolver he poisons himself with "a little
phial". And many of the stories are set abroad, particularly in Paris,
where sexual liaisons could not only exist but be seen to exist.

The deaths which occur so frequently and which are used so
predictably in order to resolve emotional deadlocks, are, on the
whole, sketchily and unconvincingly described; but then they are
more symbolic than real. Unconsciously the writers of these bizarre
stories must have felt that death provided the only euphemism
sufficiently powerful and portentous to substitute for the situations
they actually wanted to talk about; death was capable of standing for
castration, impotence, etiolation or just plain spinelessness, in short,
any of the states to which, they feared, a woman might reduce a man
if she took up arms against the sexual hierarchy of the day.

Who was this terrifying and destructive New Woman?

To *Punch* she was, naturally, a huge joke. Determined to reassure
its largely male readership, it was constantly cracking rib-ticklers at
her expense:

> "I say, Tibbins, old man, is it true that your wife has been asked to
> resign at the Omphale club?"
> "Well yes; you see the Committee found that she was guilty of
> ungentlemanly behaviour." (5 January 1895)

> "By the way Doctor, the 'new Woman', don'tcherknow—what'll
> she be like, when she's grown old?"
> "My Dear Colonel, she'll never grow old."
> "Great Scott! You don't mean she's going to last for ever!"
> "She won't even last the century! She's got every malady under
> the sun!" (13 April 1895)

If jokes could kill, the nineteenth century would be strewn with *Punch*'s victims, all brutally clubbed to death. As a barometer of middle-class prejudice it must be unsurpassed, but like all registers of prejudice, as fast as it dispensed disapproval it advertised its fears. Although suffering from no gentlemanly inhibitions when it came to vilifying the New Woman, it was clearly rattled by her. With more optimism than accuracy, it depicted her as a normal, wholesome girl, with all her mother's normal, wholesome instincts, who had, alas, been subverted, evilly influenced and generally led astray. *The Yellow Book* was frequently pointed to as the kind of pernicious propaganda likely to poison the pure well of womanhood.

Husbands and admirers of the screaming sisterhood were regarded as particularly preposterous. In, for example, "She Notes" (10 March 1894) by Borgia Smudgiton with Japanese Fan de Siécle Illustrations by Mortarthurio Whiskersly, the following piece of domestic dialogue is overheard:

"Off your pipe, old chappie. Feel a bit cheap?" (It is her husband who speaks this way.)
"Yes, beastly, thanks old man!" (He dispenses a restorative whisky—neat, of course; "soda's for boys".)
"What's your book?"
"O, one of Wilde's little things. I like Wilde; he shocks the middle classes. Only the middle classes are so easily shocked!"

The joke, presumably, lies in seeing what happens when you allow things to go to extremes: the man solicitously attends to his gruff mate, administers soothing drinks, and attempts to take an interest in her reading, which is of course well above his pretty head. She is moody, domineering and dissatisfied; Wilde, in her view, does not go nearly far enough. The joke, however, smacks more of fear than satire.

One can only hope that the New Woman was reassured by finding herself one of *Punch*'s regular targets—it was after all an honour she shared with most of the nineteenth century's trail-blazing men and women—and that the magazine's sententious advice and clod-hopping jokes only spurred her on to greater efforts in her quest for identity. Inherent in these jokes are, however, the same fears that permeate *The Yellow Book* series, and their effect on any woman who regarded herself as New must, once her initial indignation had abated, have been highly disturbing. She, no less than *Punch*, did not wish to see her husband transformed into the pathetic creature so vividly envisioned by Borgia Smudgiton, and yet in 1894 this must have seemed to be precisely the risk she was taking.

Fortunately their morbid literary preoccupations did not in any way repress the women contributors to *The Yellow Book*, most of whom led vigorous, passionate lives, wrote prolifically and successfully and survived to ripe old ages. They conducted their lives according to the most *avant-garde* principles, and their behaviour seems to radiate none of the fearful caution that characterises their *Yellow Book* fiction.

"Graham Tomson", for instance, deserted her husband, Arthur Tomson, artist and member of the New English Art Club, for H. B. Marriot Watson with whom she lived in order to provide grounds for divorce. In time she married Marriot Watson, and poems by her appear in *The Yellow Book* under both names. Mene Muriel Dowie was both writer and explorer; she too abandoned her husband for another man, who, fittingly enough, was also an explorer. Netta Syrett, who died in 1940, and Ethel Colburn Mayne, who died in 1941, both published innumerable novels. Ethel Sharpe, who died in 1945, became a suffragette at the turn of the century and fought indefatigably for that and many other causes throughout her long life; she also wrote regularly for *The Guardian*. Ada Leverson has passed into legend as Wilde's Sphinx, the woman who protected and housed him when he was on bail before his trial, and more or less a fugitive. She contributed two stories to the magazine and wrote a number of novels. Most of the other women displayed a similar energy and an admirable capacity for maintaining emotional stability within unconventional relationships despite the prevailing moral disapproval of the day.

These achievements, mundane enough in themselves, provide a startling contrast to the pattern of failure and inadequacy that typified the lives of so many of the male contributors. Compared to the vitality and productivity of the women, the debility of the men looks positively eerie, and almost suggests that everyone's worse fears, including *Punch*'s, did come true and that the women did indeed suck their new-found vigour from the veins of their men.

Punch found the Decadent poets supremely ridiculous and contemptible:

Algie: What's the matter Archie? You're not looking well.
Archie: You wouldn't look well, if you'd been suffering from insomnia every afternoon for a week. (27 October 1894)

Not content with jokes it committed its scorn to verse:

> *To Any Boy-Poet of the Decadence*
>   For your dull little vices we don't care a fig,
>   It is *this* we deeply deplore;
>   You were cast for a common or usual pig,
>   But you play the invincible bore.

Cartoon decadents are depicted as weak-chinned, wilting youths whose pipe-stem necks are barely capable of upholding their ludicrous bow-ties.

Physical frailty and "petty vice" do in fact characterize the so-called decadent writers, and the roll-call of their deaths makes grim reading. Yeats referred to his friends of the Rhymer Club days as The Tragic Generation, and not without reason.

Tuberculosis killed both Beardsley and Harland. Hubert Crackanthorpe drowned himself at the age of twenty-six in the Seine after his wife had left him for another man, although, typically, he had spent the same night discussing the situation with friends and family and had defended her behaviour. John Davidson drowned himself in the Cornish Sea, at the age of forty-two, leaving a suicide note: "The time has come to make an end. There are several motives. I find my pension not enough; I have therefore still to turn aside and attempt things for which people will pay. My health also counts. Asthma and other annoyances I have tolerated for years; but I cannot put up with cancer . . ." Charles Conder, also tubercular, died at the age of forty-one, drunk and melancholic. Lionel Johnson died at thirty-five. Ernest Dowson died of self-neglect as much as anything at the age of thirty-two. Arthur Symons lived to the exceptional age of eighty, but spent many years in an asylum, the same one in which Conder died. Symons has written that he knew twelve men who killed themselves.

Physical enfeeblement, a savage need for self-abasement and a devastating inability to establish and sustain sexual relationships compound the uniform misery of their lives. Ernest Dowson, for example, permanently destitute and frequently drunk, developed a passion for the twelve-year-old daughter of a Soho restaurant owner, Adelaide Foltinowicz, known as Missie. Night after night he played chess with her father in order to be near his beloved. He did all he could to impress her mother with his eligibility as a suitor. He dedicated verses to her (1896): "For Adelaide. To you who are my verses, as on some future day, if you ever care to read them, you will understand." She never did understand, and, prosaically enough, gave her heart instead to a tailor who had once worked in the restaurant, and married him. In his story "Apple Blossom in Brittany" (Volume III), he idealized his hopeless romance: an English critic falls in love with his teenage French ward, proposes marriage, but cannot bring himself to persuade her when she voices her doubts, and finally returns her to her convent. "Any other ending to his love," he reflects, "had been an impossible grossness, and that to lose her in just that fashion was the only way in which he could keep her always. And his acquiescence was without bitterness, and attended only by that indefinable sadness which to a man of his temper was but the last refinement of pleasure." His life was one of unrelieved tragedy; his father poisoned himself, his mother put a noose round her neck, and he himself died of tuberculosis in 1900, penniless, starved and alcoholic.

George Gissing fell victim to another neurosis, typical of this blighted generation: he was obsessed by prostitutes. He was dismissed from Owen's College, Manchester, and imprisoned for stealing money which he had given to a street-walker. He subsequently married her and lived unhappily with her for six years until she left him and went back to the streets. He saw her once again, in 1888, when he was summoned to a room in a Lambeth slum where she had been found dead. His second wife was a servant girl whom he picked up in Regent's Park. He was no happier with her and finally left her for a Frenchwoman with whom he lived, more or less contentedly, until he died of pneumonia in 1903 at the age of forty-six. His second wife ultimately went mad. Throughout his life he consistently befriended and helped prostitutes, and through them he seemed to be trying to find a way of coming to terms with the erotic conditions and confusions of his day. He was not interested in the comparatively respectable "mistresses" who served the bourgeoisie and lived in lucrative seclusion in St John's Wood, but was fascinated by the ragged, impoverished, gin-addicted waifs on whom Jack the Ripper preyed in 1887. Their wretchedness both appalled and excited him and he was realistic enough to offer them what they needed most, not religious solace or rustic exile, but hard cash.

In France the prostitute was, if not respected, at least acknowledged; she was licensed by the police and protected from many of the humiliations her English sister was obliged to endure; she was painted by many of the Impressionists, notably Toulouse-Lautrec, and writers like the de Goncourt brothers, Balzac, Baudelaire, Dumas Fils, and Zola elevated her to the status of heroine. Conditions were, however, very different in England, where an enormous army of unmentionable prostitutes daily marched the streets catering for every class and taste, where a huge but clandestine trade in pornography flourished, but where the prostitute as a literary subject was virtually taboo. In Victorian literature it is almost impossible to find a novel in which such a woman plays an important role. The double standard imposed a stern regime and the artist who dared to challenge it did so at his peril. When, for instance, Bernard Shaw attempted to produce his play *Mrs Warren's Profession*, in which his heroine decided that to turn prostitute was preferable to working in a white lead factory, the Lord Chamberlain refused to grant a licence.

Bearing in mind the sinister comparison with their female contemporaries, it is impossible not to feel that these men found the conventions which were supposed in their day to govern and maintain sexual relationships totally inadequate and treacherous. The confident, measured stride of Victorian manhood had, by the nineties, begun to falter and trip. The threats and demands represented by the ever accelerating movement towards female emancipation on all fronts, seems to have unnerved and unbalanced this group of men and driven them to seek comfort and oblivion in homosexuality, prostitution, addiction to alcohol and opiates, sterile relationships with children, and, in some cases, forlorn celibacy.

In this context, it is difficult to regard the Decadents as a band of daring and iconoclastic rebels; they look far more like refugees fleeing in the face of bewildering social evolutions. Their output, by Victorian standards, was diminutive and pale. Their poems were short and their emotional range extremely limited; their prose is largely confined to essays, short stories, fragments and prose fancies; their leading artist worked exclusively in black and white; their work is often narcissistic and precious. And yet it is in this paleness that their fascination lies, for it represents a desperate and feverish attempt to escape both from the hideousness of industrialized Victorian England and from the very developments that were putting an axe to the root of the world they found so insupportable.

It is curious, but somehow fitting, that the decade should be dominated by Beardsley, a consumptive in his twenties whose *oeuvre* consisted entirely of black and white drawings. In his *Yellow Book* illustrations women predominate as subjects and his attitude to female sexuality was far more direct and provocative than any of the other contributors, which perhaps explains why the reviewers condemned his work so venomously. They not only attacked him personally but also dismissed his drawings as evil, ugly and plain bad. "Who wants these fantastic pictures," asked the *World*, "like

Japanese sketches gone mad, of a woman with a black tuft for a head, and snake-like fingers starting off the key-board of a piano; of Mrs Patrick Campbell with a black sticking-plaister hat, hunchy shoulders, a happily impossible waist, and a yard and half of indefinable skirt . . ." Beardsley's women, declared *The National Observer* critic, "resemble nothing on the earth, nor in the firmament that is above the earth, nor in the water under the earth, with their lips of a more than Hottentot thickness, their bodies of a lath-like flatness, their impossibly pointed toes and fingers, and their small eyes which have the form and comeliness of an unshelled snail."

The world inhabited by his figures is essentially artificial; the clothes they wear are elaborate, preposterous, and, above all, suggestive; their rooms and gardens are sheer masquerade; men and women alike wear masks, cosmetics, beauty spots and absurdly elaborate coiffures; their bodies are often unnaturally elongated, and their feet reduced to miniatures; they keep company with satyrs, pierrots, embryos and grotesques. His scenes are lit by candles, foot-lights, gas-lights, or an unearthly twilight, but, whatever the source, shadows are never cast.

Although none of *The Yellow Book* drawings are explicitly erotic, they all emanate an erotic nuance, and this insinuating quality, together with the indiscriminate and shameless hints of lesbianism, homosexuality, transvestism, and of other, more shadowy vices, must have particularly aggravated the critics. His women in no way conform to the conventions of Victorian feminity: they are not pure or sweet or noble; they are not motherly or infantile; they do not remotely represent chastity, innocence or sanctity. Nudity in art was acceptable, indeed positively welcome to the Victorians, but Beardsley's women are seldom nude; on the contrary they are deliberately dressed to attract and provoke. His women are eager to be observed. They seem to take the viewer into their confidence, inviting him to share their intimacies; they tease, they challenge, and occasionally they even wink at the onlooker. Above all, his women are knowing. They know about sex, and are manifestly keen to indulge their knowledge.

His title "*L'Education Sentimentale*", for example, makes it clear, not that the drawing needs any clarification, that the subject is erotic: the taller figure of the crone on the left is obscenely raddled; the young girl on the left is winking mischievously and making it obvious that there is not much the older woman can teach her. Her pose, a piece of calculated insolence on Beardsley's part, is a wicked caricature of the conventional concept of little-girl innocence. Nothing, it must have seemed to the critics, was sacred to this monster. The scene is rendered totally theatrical by the curving line that separates the two figures and culminates in a loose fold of drapery—a typical Beardsley gesture.

"Nightpiece", the drawing which immediately precedes Symon's "Stella Maris" is also deliberately provocative. The drawing is entirely black except for a grey building looming in the background and the stark white of the girl's face, bosom and foot. She is on the streets, unaccompanied and luridly dressed. Her expression is enigmatic and private. If she is a prostitute, and that seems to be the implication, she clearly feels no guilt or embarrassment. She is doing precisely what Victorian women were meant not to do, particularly in the pages of a fashionable literary quarterly: she is advertising her sexuality.

Holbrook Jackson, in his masterly account of the 1890s, said of Beardsley that he was an intellectual artist, "drawing the thing as he *thought* it". Beardsley, he maintained, was "the most literary of all modern artists; his drawings are never the outcome of observation— they are always the outcome of thought; they are thoughts become pictures. And even then they are rarely if ever the blossoming of thought derived from experience; they are the hot-house growths of thought derived from books, pictures and music. Beardsley always worked indoors, without models and by artificial, generally, candle, light." Presumably *The National Observer* critic would have quarrelled with none of this, but it was those very "thoughts become pictures" that so revolted him and confirmed his worst suspicions regarding the Decadents. By giving flesh to decadent fantasy Beardsley not only made a brazen mockery of decency and morality, he also advanced a monstrously perverted vision of womanhood, a vision doubly damnable for its uncomfortable similarity to the portrait proposed by certain extremists among women themselves. It is not surprising that *Punch* felt obliged to warn its lady readers against the malignant consequences of dabbling in *The Yellow Book*.

IV

A cynic might be entitled to ask why the magazine folded. If, he might enquire, it was so fascinating and sold so well, if it was so beloved by those in the fashionable know, and so loathed by those critics whose vilification could be relied on to further recommend it to the *avant-garde*, if it was so compelling even when it was bad, why then did it peter out after only thirteen volumes?

The answer must be pure conjecture since Lane and Harland were understandably tight-lipped on the subject.

Beardsley's dismissal cannot be accounted the reason. It is true that whatever he did was news, and that his drawings, along with other controversial contributions, provoked just the kind of publicity that a publisher hopes for when launching a new venture. But by the fifth volume the magazine had been in existence for more than a year and its reputation must have been firmly established. It is also true that Lane's experience during the Wilde scandal had taught him that pulling the bourgeois tail was a lucrative business until the victim chose to retaliate, and thereafter he probably discouraged any potentially lubricous contributions. He certainly never found another artist of Beardsley's calibre. The standard however of many of the later nine volumes is just as high, if anything higher, than the first four: Henry James, Arnold Bennett, H. G. Wells, Baron Corvo, John Buchan, George Gissing, Edmund Gosse and W. B. Yeats for instance all appear in the later so-called grey volumes.

There is, on the other hand, no question that editorial inspiration seems to flag badly towards the end; the same writers reappear again and again, Harland's own contributions increase in number and length, and the volumes begin to fall into a disappointingly predictable pattern. This was not necessarily Harland's fault, who appears to have been conscientious and industrious throughout; the reason lies perhaps in the very nature of the magazine itself. Four times a year Harland was required to produce a lengthy volume comprising prose, verse and illustrations of the highest quality; it proved to be a feat beyond even his exceptional capability.

At the funeral, John Lane remarked that the magazine had failed to pay dividends, a direct reference presumably to declining sales figures. The magazine's design and production were lavish, and in the early volumes positively extravagant, and its price—five shillings—was by no means exorbitant; healthy sales therefore were certainly needed to cover costs alone. But Lane was probably also referring to dividends of another kind. He had backed the magazine in order to advertise his list and attract new authors. The Wilde scandal had rebounded badly on him and given rise to publicity of the most damaging kind, from which he only recovered by playing safe with both his list and *The Yellow Book*. New authors, whose work appeared in the magazine, certainly joined his list—Wells and Bennett among them—but he must have concluded that Harland's ability to recruit new blood was no better than his own, a conclusion which automatically jeopardized the magazine's continuing existence. *The Yellow Book* was terminated not because of any inherent inadequacy in its contents but largely because it had ceased to command the enthusiasm of its proprietor and had ceased to serve his interests.

The volume dated April 1897 was the last to appear. It was published late and *The Times* did not miss its opportunity: "*The Yellow Book*, though it has outlived its youthful wildness keeps up a reputation for eccentricity by producing its April number . . . in May." No announcement of the magazine's decease was made; no explanation was offered.

The Yellow Book

An Illustrated Quarterly

Volume III   October, 1894

London : John Lane, The Bodley Head, Vigo Street
Boston : Copeland & Day
Agents for the Colonies : Robt. A. Thompson & Co.

The Dead Wall

By H. B. Marriott Watson

THE dawn stared raw and yellow out of the east at Rosewarne. Its bleak and ugly face smouldered through morose vapours. The wind blew sharp against the windows, shaking them in their casements. The prospect from that lonely chamber overawed him with menace ; it glowered upon him. The houses in the square, wrapped in immitigable gloom, were to him ominous memorials of death. They frightened him into a formless panic. Anchored in that soundless sea, they terrified him with their very stillness. In dreary ranks they rose, a great high wall of doom, lifting their lank chimneys to the dreadful sky. They obsessed him with forebodings to which he could put no term, for which he could find no reason. Shrouded under its great terror, his poor mind fell into deeper depression under the influence of those malign and ugly signals. He strove to withdraw his thoughts and direct them upon some different subject. He wrenched them round to the contemplation of his room, his walls, his wife. A dull pain throbbed in the back of his head. He repeated aloud the topics upon which he would have his mind revolve, but the words rang in his ears without meaning. He touched the pictures on the wall, he spoke their names, he covered his face and strained hard to recapture coherent thought. The subjects mocked him : they were too

nimble

nimble and elusive for his tired brain ; they danced out of reach, and he followed blindly till a deeper darkness fell. They grew faint and shadowy, like wraiths in a mist, and he pursued the glancing shadows. Finally, his brain grew blank ; it was as if consciousness had lapsed ; and he found himself regarding a fly that crawled upon the pane. Outside lay the oppression of that appalling scene that horrified him—he knew not why.

Rosewarne was growing used to these nervous exhibitions. This unequal struggle had been repeated through many weeks, but he had always so far come out of it with personal security. The dread that some day he would fail continually haunted him, and increased the strain of the conflict. He wondered what lay at the back of this horrible condition, and shuddered as he wondered. And he knew now that he must not let himself adrift, but must dispose the devils by every means. He broke into a whistle, and moved about the room carelessly. It was a lively stave from the streets that his lips framed, but it conveyed to him no sense of sound. He perambulated the chamber with a false air of cheerfulness. He eyed the bed with his head askew, winking as if to share a jest with it. He patted the pillows, arranging and disarranging them in turn. He laughed softly, merrily, emptily. He seized the dumb-bells from the mantelpiece and whirled them about his head ; he chafed his hands, he rubbed his flesh. Little by little the blood moved with more content through his body, and the pulse of his heart sank slowly.

Outside, the dawn brightened and the wind came faster. Rose-warne looked forth and nodded ; then he turned and left the room, his face flashing as he passed the mirror, like the distempered face of a corpse. Across the landing he paused before a door, and, bending to the keyhole, listened ; little low sounds of life came to his ears, and suddenly his haggard face crowded with emotions. He

He rose and softly descended the stairs to his study. The house lay in the quiet of sleep, and within the solitude of that rich room he, too, was as still as the sleepers. The inferior parts of the window formed a blind of stained glass, but the grey light flowed through the upper panes into a magnificent wilderness. The cold ashes of the fire, by which he had sat at his task late into the morning, lay still within the grate. The little ensigns of a human presence, the scattered papers, the dirty hearth, all the instruments of his work, looked mean and squalid within the spacious dignity of that high room. He lit the gas and sat down to his table, moving his restless fingers among the papers. It was as if his members arrogantly claimed their independence, and refused the commands of a weak brain. His mind had abrogated. His hands shifted furtively like the hands of a pickpocket: they wandered among the papers and returned to him. The clock droned out the hour slowly, and at that he started, shook his wits together, and began in haste to turn about the documents. He knew now the sheet of which he had sent his hands in quest. Large and blue and awful, it had been his ghost throughout the night. He could see the figures scrawled upon it in his own tremulous writing, rows upon rows of them, thin and sparse and self-respecting at the top, but to the close, fevered, misshapen, and reckless, fighting and jostling in a crowd for space upon the page. He laid his hand upon the horrible thing ; he opened his ledgers ; and sat deciphering once more his own ruin.

The tragedy lay bare to his shrinking eyes ; it leaped forth at him from the blurred and confused figures. There was no need to rehearse them ; he had reiterated them upon a hundred scrolls in a hundred various ways these many weeks. They had become his enemies, to deceive whom he had invoked the wreck of a fine intelligence. He had used all the wiles and dodges of a cunning
mind

mind to entrap them to his service. He had spent a weary campaign upon them, storming them with fresh troops of figures, deploying and ambuscading with all the subterfuge of a subtle business mind. But there now, as at the outset of his hopeless fight, the issue remained unchanged; the terrible sum of his sin abided, unsubtracted, undivided, unabridged. As he regarded it at this moment it seemed to assume quickly a vaster proportion. His crime cried out upon him, calling for vengeance in his ears. Seizing a pen, eagerly, vacantly, he set forth anew to recompose the items.

Rosewarne worked on for a couple of hours, holding his quivering fingers to the paper by the sheer remnants of his will. His brain refused its offices, and he stumbled among the numerical problems with false and blundering steps. To add one sum to another he must ransack the litter of his mind; the knowledge that runs glibly to the tongue of a child he must rediscover by persistent and arduous concentration. But still he kept his seat, and jotted down his cyphers. About him the house stirred slowly; noises passed his door and faded; the grim and yellow sun rose higher and struck upon the table, contending with the gaslight. But Rosewarne paid no heed; he wrestled with his numb brain and his shivering fingers, wrestled to the close of the page; where once more the hateful figures gleamed in bold ink, menacing and blinking, his old ghost renewed and invested with fresh life.

The pen dropped from his hand, his head fell upon his arms, and as he lay in that helpless attitude of despair that protests not, of misery that can make no appeal, the door fell softly open and his wife entered.

"Freddy, whatever are you doing here like this?" she said, with surprise in her voice. "Have you gone to sleep?"

Rosewarne

Rosewarne lifted his head sharply and turned to her. Athwart the pallor of his face gleamed for an instant a soft flush of pleasure, and his dull eyes lit up with affection.

"I was doing some work, Dorothy," said he, "and I was tired."

Mrs. Rosewarne took a step nearer. Her fine grey eyes regarded him with wonder and with inquiry, and in her voice a little impatience mingled with a certain kindliness.

"It's very absurd your working like this," she said, "and in this cold room without a fire? Aren't you coming to breakfast?"

Rosewarne got up from his chair. "Why, yes," he laughed. "Of course. I didn't realise it was ready. Oh, Dolly dear," he paused and put his hand to his head with a look of perplexity; then his face lightened. "Dolly, I've got something for you."

"For me!" she asked, and the curve of her lips drooped in a pretty smile of curiosity.

He fumbled in a drawer and withdrew a packet.

"Yes, darling. You know what day it is. It's your birthday, and you're twenty——"

"Oh, for goodness' sake, Freddy, don't," she interrupted with a touch of impatience; and then opening the packet examined the contents with care. The light dawned in her eyes. "How very pretty! I was in need of a bracelet. Freddy, you are a good boy. But come, you mustn't catch cold. Come into the dining-room, and get warm, you simpleton."

She patted him softly on the head, and fell again to the scrutiny of her present. Rosewarne did not move, but watched her, smiling. "Aren't you coming?" she asked, looking up at last.

His eyes met hers and pleaded with them dumbly, but she made no sign, returning once more to her jewels.

"Isn't

"Isn't it worth a kiss, Dolly ? " he asked softly.

Mrs. Rosewarne looked at him vaguely. "What ! Oh, well, yes, if you like, I suppose." She bent towards him, and he touched her cheek gently. "But it was very nice of you to think of me," she said, withdrawing. "Come to breakfast now."

Rosewarne followed her into the breakfast-room, with a fresh access of impotence. He fumbled with his chair ; the napkin fluttered out of his fingers ; he pulled a plate to him, and the silver rattled under his clumsy action ; a fork clattered to the floor. Mrs. Rosewarne winced.

"How very stupid you are to-day, Freddy ! " she said pettishly.

He laughed a short meaningless laugh, and begged her pardon. Her movements were full of gentle grace ; her breath came easily and with the best breeding. Her teacup tinkled sweetly, and only that and the soft sussurra of her sleeves marked her stately presence at the table. She looked at the bracelet comfortably, and lifted her cup to her lips. Rosewarne glanced at her timidly. The sickly light shone clear upon the fine contours of her placid face ; the evil magic of that dreary day was transmuted upon her hair. She set down her cup and met his eyes.

"What a dreadful colour you are ! " she said critically. The ghastly yellow of his face repelled her. "I wish you would get better, and not rise at such ridiculous hours."

"I slept ill, Dolly," he answered with a faint smile. He resumed his breakfast feverishly. The knuckles of his hands seemed to stand out awkwardly ; his elbows waggled ; he mouthed at his food in a frightened fashion.

"Good heavens, Freddy," cried his wife, wrinkling her nose in distaste, "why do you eat like that ? It's more like an animal than a human being. Your manners are becoming perfectly awful."

He

He started and dropped his knife. "What the devil does it matter how I eat?" he exclaimed angrily. "You—you——" His ideas faded from him, and he sat staring at her in vacant indignation. Then he put his hand to his head. "Oh, forgive me, Dolly; forgive me, please. I'm tired and——"

"My dear man," broke in Mrs. Rosewarne coldly, "if you will make yourself ill, what can you expect?" She unfolded a morning paper and ran her eyes down the columns; Rosewarne sat looking across the room into the fire. Suddenly she called to him in a new voice. "Mr. Maclagan came to town yesterday, Freddy, and paid a visit to Downing Street."

"Yes?" he said, starting again.

She drew down the paper and looked at him over the edge, her eyes filled with some excitement.

"Do you hear, Freddy dear? Now is your chance to make the arrangement final."

He gazed at her, his face contorted in a desperate attempt to concentrate his thoughts upon her words. What was she saying? And what did it mean?

"Freddy, don't you hear?" she cried again in a voice in which impatience blended with a certain eagerness. She leaned forward and put a hand upon his arm. He clutched at it feverishly with his fingers. "Lord Hambleton is favourable, I know, and it only remains to secure Maclagan," she went on quickly. "He, you know, was inclined to agree when you saw him before. I'm sure that the nail is ready for the hammer. There is South Wiltshire, where you are known, and no one yet settled upon by the Party. See, dear; you must call on him to-day, and that, with another cheque for the Party, should place the matter beyond doubt. Freddy! Freddy! Don't you hear what I'm saying. For goodness' sake, don't look like a corpse, if you are ill."

"Yes,

"Yes, yes, Dolly," said Rosewarne hurriedly.

"And for the love of decency, don't Dolly me," said Mrs. Rosewarne with a petulant movement of her shoulders. "It's bad enough to have to answer to an elderly Quaker name like Dorothy."

Rosewarne got up from the table. "For God's sake, be civil to me, if you can't be kind," he said sharply. She regarded him coldly. "What is it you want?" he asked.

Mrs. Rosewarne rapped her knuckles angrily upon the table.

"I imagined we had made that pretty clear between us long ago," she said with a sarcastic emphasis; "we agreed that you were to go into Parliament, and we laid our plans to that end. The only thing wanting was the particular seat, and now it's found you ask me what I'm talking about."

She looked at him with placid disdain. Rosewarne shuddered; he remembered now, as in a dream, the ambitions she had formed for him.

"No, no, dear," he said. "Tell me. It's all right. I'll see Lord—Lord Hambleton. The——"

Mrs. Rosewarne's expression turned swiftly to complacency.

"No," she said, "leave him to me, Freddy. I shall see him this afternoon at the Charters's. You must see Maclagan to-day, and we'll meet and talk the matter over at dinner."

She smiled upon him with a tolerant air of patronage. Rosewarne stood by the window, restlessly twitching his fingers.

"You will not be in to lunch?" he asked, dully.

"No; I'm going to the Charters's. We have each a long day before us. It's a sort of crisis in our lives. I'm tired of this undistinguished competence. Any one can be the partner in a bank. It is the House that opens the gate to success."

She rose and swept her skirts behind her with a motion of her

arm

arm. She regarded herself in the mirror with a face of satisfaction, directing with nimble fingers an errant lock of her hair.

"And now you'll be off, I suppose," she said, and turned on him laughing. "Well, Freddy, pluck up your heart and speak your best ; you have a tongue as neat as any one when you like. Don't wear so lugubrious a countenance, dear—come !"

She kissed him lightly on the forehead, laying her hands on his shoulders, her eyes sparkling with excitement. Rosewarne put out his arms and caught her. His eyes devoured her. "Kiss me again, Dolly," he sputtered. "Kiss me again. Kiss me on the lips."

She laughed, a faint colour rose in her cheeks, and she struggled in his clutch. "Dolly, Dolly !" he pleaded. A frown of embarrassment gathered in her forehead.

"Do let me go," she said sharply.

He obeyed ; his arms fell to his sides ; wistfully he watched her withdraw. Stately in her flowing, rustling robes, receding from him, she sailed through the doorway, and with the loss of that fine vision the light and the flush fell from him, and all that remained was an ignoble figure with discoloured cheeks and sunken head. In that moment and with the chill of that departing grace fresh upon him, he regarded his tragic position plainly and without illusion. The poor rags of his last unvoiced hopes dropped from his outcast soul. He had deferred the story of his ruin, in part out of shame, but much, too, out of pity, and because of some shreds of confidence in his own fortunes. And yet, implicit in that silence he had kept, but unacknowledged in his own thoughts, had been the fear of her demeanour in the crisis. He knew her for a worldly woman, clad in great aspirations ; he had taken the measure of her trivial vanities ; he had sounded the shallows of her passionless heart ; and still he had trusted, still he had nursed an

empty

empty faith in her affection. But now at this slight repulse somehow the props swayed beneath his rickety platform, and his thoughts ran in a darker current of despair. The bankruptcy, the guilt, the horror of his defalcations, were no longer the Evil to come, but merely now the steps by which he mounted to the real tragedy of his life.

Rosewarne quietly took up his hat, and drawing on his coat, passed out of the house and walked slowly towards the City.

It was upon two o'clock when Mrs. Rosewarne descended from the portico of her house and was enclosed within her landau by the footman. She was in a fervour which became her admirably ; her cheeks were touched with points of colour, and her fine eyes brightened as with the flash of steel. She itched to try the temper of her diplomacy, and, as she entered the drawing-room of her hostess, the thought that she was well equipped for the encounter filled her anew with zest. Her eyes, piercing from that handsome face, challenged the luncheon-party. Mrs. Charters gave her a loud effusive welcome, as the beauty of the entertainment, and a general murmur of greeting seemed to salute her ears. Stepping a pace from the company and engaging easily with her hostess, Mrs. Rosewarne denoted the guests with sharp glances. Of her own disposition at the table she could have no certainty ; the occasion was urgent ; and with a nod she summoned Lord Hambleton to her side.

"And you, Lord Hambleton ! " said she with a pretty air of surprise, " why, I heard you were in Scotland."

"Scotland ! " he said, shrugging his shoulders and smiling. " What ! Scotland in January, and the session like a drawn sword at one's heart."

"Ah ! " she replied, " I had forgotten the session. And yet my poor husband talks enough about it."

"Indeed ! "

"Indeed!" said the Whip with good-humour; "there is still some one, then, who bothers about us."

She lifted her shoulders slightly, as one who would disclaim a personal participation in the folly.

"Doesn't every one?" she asked.

"Why, we talk of ourselves," said he laughing, "but I did not know any one else took an interest in us. We have outlived our time, you see. We are early Victorians, so to speak. Representative government is a glorious tradition, like the English flag or Balaclava—very brave, very wonderful, but very unimportant. I know we bulk largely in the newspapers. It is our *métier*. But I wonder why. The habit exists when the utility is fled. Is it because the advertisers love us, do you think? It is the only reason I can conceive. We all owe our being to the Births, Deaths and Marriages. The servant-girl, my dear Mrs. Rosewarne, confers upon me the fame of a Tuesday's issue, for the shilling she expends upon a 'Wanted.' Alas!" He pulled his features into an expression of dismay. "When the hoarding and the sky-sign come in we shall go out."

Mrs. Rosewarne laughed gently, a demure intelligence shining from her eyes.

"And you," said he quizzically, "you don't care for us?"

"Oh, I!" she retorted with a sigh. "Yes, I talk of you. I am obliged to talk of you over the hearth-rug. I assure you I have all your names by rote, and rattle them off like a poll-parrot."

"Ah!" said Lord Hambleton, peering into her face curiously; "I can appreciate your tone. You are weary of us."

"Frankly, yes," said she, smiling. They both laughed, and he made a gesture of apology.

"Why?" he asked.

The

The voice of a butler cried from the doorway; there was a sudden stir in the room, and then a little hush.

"We are separated, alas!" said Lord Hambleton.

"Not at all," said Mrs. Charters, suddenly, at his elbow. "I believe you are neighbours."

Mrs. Rosewarne's heart bounded in her side, and then beat placidly with its accustomed rhythm. Lord Hambleton looked at her. "That's very nice," he murmured.

At the table he turned to her with an immediate air of interest. "Why?" he repeated.

Her gaze had wandered across the table with a profession of gentle indifference. She was surveying the guests with a remote abstraction; plucked out of which she glanced at him with a pretty hint of embarrassment, her forehead frowning as though to recover the topic of their conversation.

"Why?" she echoed; and then: "Oh yes," said she, smiling as out of a memory regained. "Because—well, because, what does it all avail?"

"Nothing, I grant you," he replied easily, "or very little, save to ourselves. You forget us. We have our business. Our fathers gamed and we talk. Don't forget us."

He spoke in railing tones, almost jocosely, and she lifted her eyebrows a line.

"Ah yes!" she assented. "Yes, but me and the rest of us, are we to keep you in your fun?"

He paused before replying, and noted every particular distinction in her handsome face. They were at close quarters; he leaned a trifle nearer, and lowered his voice to a mocking confidence:

"Mrs. Rosewarne, you would never blow upon us, surely." He feigned to hang in suspense upon her answer; the proximity touched

touched him with a queer elation ; she shot upon him one of her loveliest glances.

"I can hold my tongue for a friend, Lord Hambleton."

"Come," he said, nodding, "that is better. That is a very sportsmanlike spirit."

Mrs. Rosewarne considered, smiling the while she continued her meal. The approach was long, but to manœuvre heightened her spirits, and she was now to make a bolder movement.

"But why," she asked, "should you expect mercy from a woman ? "

" I don't, Heaven knows," he responded promptly ; "I wonder at it, and admire."

"I think you have had a very long innings," said she, thoughtfully, "and were it in my power I would show no mercy."

Lord Hambleton laughed contentedly. " Oh, well ! " he said.

"There is no opportunity for women," continued Mrs. Rosewarne, wistfully ; " there has never been."

"Who would have suspected that you were ambitious ? " commented Lord Hambleton, archly.

She threw up her jewelled fingers. " Ambitious ! " she said, impatiently. " I am a woman. Where is the use ? That is your business ; mine is the boudoir, naturally. We are always—in the field, you call it, don't you ? Men go to the wickets. My poor husband would tear out his heart for a seat. He is sound, he is good, he has wits, he is tolerable ; he would serve excellently well upon a minor committee, and would never give a shadow of trouble. He would never ask questions, or soar at Cabinets. Yet it is, I suppose, ambition of a kind. But me ! What has it to do with me ! A woman knows nothing—of politics, no more than life. I can enjoy no vicarious pomp. No ! give me the authority myself ;
give

give me a share in it, Lord Hambleton, and then I will tell you if I am ambitious ! "

She put her head aside, and appeared with this tirade to drop the subject ; she made a feint of listening to a conversation across the table. She smiled at the jest that reached her as if she had forgotten her companion. And yet she was aware that the aspect of her face, at which he was staring, was that which best became her. Lord Hambleton watched the long and delicate lines warm with soft blood, and his own senses were strangely affected.

"But you would influence him," he said presently. She came back with a display of reluctance, and seemed to pause, searching for his meaning.

"Oh ! " she said, "Heavens ! I have higher aims than that. Make him Under-Secretary, and he would be worth influencing ; but poor Freddy——" She shrugged her shoulders and looked away again, as though impatient of the subject. Perhaps she was really tired of the conversation, he reflected.

"Well, here we are," he said, with deprecation in his voice, "talking all the time on a subject which you professed at the outset bored you. How unpardonable of me ! "

"Bored me ! " she said, opening her eyes at him and very innocently. "Oh, not talking with any one worth while."

Lord Hambleton's eyes dropped, and he was silent. The wine had fired his blood no less than her beauty. He looked up again, and met her glance by misadventure. A show of colour flooded her face ; the pulses beat in her white throat. He did not know why, but his hands trembled a little, and a bar seemed broken down between them.

"Upon my soul ! " he said, with an excited laugh, "I believe you would regenerate us all, if you were in the House ! "

"I'm sure I should," she said gaily. Her heart fluttered in
her

her side. "But there is no chance of that; I could only keep a *salon*. Why isn't it done? There is no Recamier nowadays; there is no Blessington. There is even no Whip's wife."

She was conscious of a faint shudder as she made this impudent stroke, and withdrew in a tremble into herself. She lay back in her chair, frightened. The words fell opportunely into Lord Hambleton's heart; he had no suspicion that they were deliberate, and the blood danced lightly along his arteries.

"You would hold a *salon* bravely," he said.

"Try me," she said with the affectation of playful laughter.

He laughed with her, and "Oh, we shall have everything out of you by-and-bye," said he. "We will bide our time. What we want just now more than anything is sound men. Now Mr. Rosewarne——"

"Poor Freddy is as sound as Big Ben, I suppose," said Mrs. Rosewarne, indifferently.

She felt the blood burning in her cheeks. Their eyes encountered. It seemed to him that they had a private secret together. He scarce knew what it was, so far had his sensations crowded upon his intelligence; but some connection, woven through the clatter of that public meal, held him and her in common. With her quick wit she was aware of his thought. She felt flushed with her own beauty. It was not of her husband he was thinking, and she was aware that he believed she too was not considering him. The understanding lay between themselves. She rose triumphant; her heart spoke in loud acclamations.

"Ah, well," she said, with a tiny sigh, "I must wait, then, for old age to found my *salon*."

"No," he replied, smiling at her; "and why? We must have your husband in the House. Then you may begin at once."

"My

"My husband!" she echoed, as though recalled to some vague and distasteful consideration.

"Yes. You must have this *salon*. It may save us."

She looked at him, as if in doubt. He rose beside her. He overtopped her by a head, and a certain strength about his forehead attracted her. Ah! If this had been her husband! The regret flashed and was gone.

"Come and tell him," she said suddenly.

He misinterpreted the fervour in her eyes. "When?" he asked.

"To-night," she murmured.

There was a momentary pause, and then, "To-night," he assented, taking her hand.

Mrs. Rosewarne moved easily within the retinue of her admirers in the drawing-room. She regarded the company with cool eyes of triumph. She held their gazes; the looks they passed upon her fed her complacency; she was sensible of her new distinction among them. And when, later, she returned to her house, she was still under the escort of success. The excitement ran like rich wine in her body, and under its stimulus her pale face was flushed with a tide of colour. She dressed for dinner, radiant, and crowned, as she conceived, with incomparable splendour. The presiding enthusiasm of her mind prevailed upon her beauty. In the glass she considered her looks, and smilingly softened the glory of her cheeks. Her thoughts reverted with amiable contempt to her husband, and in a measure he too was exalted in her own triumph. She descended the stairs, and swept into the dining-room in the full current of her happiness; and she had a sudden sense of repulse upon finding the room vacant.

"Where is your master?" she asked of the servant, who stood in observant silence at the further end of the room.

Williams

Williams had seen him come in an hour ago ; he had retired to his room. Should he go and inquire ?

"No : we will give him a few minutes," said she, seating herself.

She held communion with her own surprises. She anticipated his sensations ; if he had failed with Maclagan, she, at least, had had better fortune, and for a moment Freddy and she were wrapt in common fellowship, set upon a common course. But as the time wore on, and he made no appearance, she grew restless and fidgeted ; a little annoyance mingled with her good-humour ; the warmth of her success ebbed away. She despatched Williams to bring the laggard down, and when he had returned with the report that he could get no answer, she picked up her skirts, and with lowering brows herself undertook the mission.

Mrs. Rosewarne paused outside her husband's room, and knocked. There was no response, and turning the handle of the door impatiently, she entered. The lamp burned low, and Freddy lay upon the bed, sprawling in an attitude of graceless comfort. The noise of his hard breathing sounded in the chamber, and the odour of strong spirit filled the air. In an access of angry disgust she shook him by the shoulders, and he lifted a stupid face to her, his eyes shot with blood.

"Is it you, Dolly ? " he asked thickly.

Her voice rose on a high note of anger.

"Do you know that the gong has gone this half-hour ? Bah ! You have been drinking, you beast ! "

He sat up, staring at her vacantly, and slowly his eyes grew quick with life and fury.

"And what the devil is it to you if I have ? " he said savagely. "Why, in hell's name, don't you leave me alone ? What are

you

you doing here? What are you doing in my room? It was you relegated me to this. What are you doing here?"

"I came," said she coldly, "to call you to dinner; but since you have chosen to be the beast you are, I will leave you."

At the word, she swept upon her heel and was gone. Rosewarne sat for some minutes dully upon his bed. The flame of his anger had leapt and died, and he was now hunched up physically and morally, like a craven: his wits dispersed, his mind groping in a dreadful space for some palpable occasion of pain. Presently his reason flowed once more, and piece by piece he resumed the horrible round of life. Thereafter came a deep, warm gush of reason and affection. He had been brutal; he had been the beast she termed him. He had used her evilly when she meant but kindly by him. His heart wept for her and for himself—she was his love and his darling. He would go and pour forth his tears of regret upon her. She had naturally been struck to the heart to see him thus unmanned and sapped in the very foundations of his mind. She did not know. How could she? . . . . But he must tell her! The thought fetched him to a sudden term in the maudlin consideration of his streaming emotions. Drawn at this instant before the presence of that Terror, he trembled and rocked upon his couch. He threw the gathering thoughts aside. He must not suffer them to cloud his mind again. He must go forth and enter the room with the pleading face of a penitent. It was her due; it was his necessity—nay, this control was demanded by the very terms of his being.

He set his dress in order; he combed himself before the glass, and regarded his own grimacing image. "I will think of nothing," he murmured. "I am a man. There is nothing wrong. I can assume that for an hour. I shall go straight to Dolly. I must ward it all off. It will suffice later. Now! I am am going to begin—Now! I will think of nothing. Do you hear, you fool! Oh, you damned, silly fool! You know it is fatal if you don't. Stop. No figures; no worries. Just thrust them aside. It can't matter that two and two make four when they ought to make five. Now then! From this moment I stop. I am a man," he explained to his grimacing image. "No more figures. I will begin. No worries! Now!" He pulled out his watch. "In five seconds I will start." He saw the hand jump round. "Now!" and then in the ear of his brain a thin voice cried, softly insistent: "Five thousand and that odd two hundred. Is that all right? Go back on it. Give them just a glance." He paused, but the blood in his head stood still. At the cross ways he trembled, dazed with the conflict of the two desires. "Well, one glance."

At that the whole body of his madness rolled back upon him through the rift. He threw up his hands, and, hiding his face in the bed-clothes, groaned. "Now!" he said again, flinging himself peremptorily to his feet. He straightened his figure. "Now!" As if with a wild, reckless motion, he pulled to the door of his mind, and shutting his eyes, marched out of the room, laughing mechanically. "Dorothy, Dorothy, Dorothy!" he muttered under his breath.

Rosewarne entered the dining-room with a quick tread and a moving galvanic smile.

"Dolly, forgive me," he said; "I am late. Where are you? Oh, Williams, some fish. That will do."

He started to talk in a very hurried manner, but with humble cheerfulness. His wife stared at him coldly, answering in short, colourless sentences. But he made amends for her reticence with a continuous stream of talk. He chattered freely, and he ate ravenously. He rambled on through numberless topics with no

apparent

apparent connection. All the reserves of his nature were enrolled in that gallant essay to fence him from the Horror of his life, and hedge him safely about with casual trifles. Of a sudden he saw things clear about him. A certain bright wit shone in his soliloquies; he spoke with that incoherence and irresponsibility which begets sometimes effective phrasing. His wife considered him; the novelty of his conversation struck her, its frivolity took her with admiration. Slowly the barriers of her own reserve broke down, the sense of satisfaction in herself grew upon her, and by degrees her good-humour returned. She joined in his talk, laughed a little, was inspired by his mood into newer, fresher, wilder hopes. No word was said about the scene in the bedroom; it had dropped into past history, and their feet were set to the future. And when Williams was gone, she turned swiftly upon him, her zeal showing in her eyes.

"And now, Freddy," she said, "tell me all about Maclagan."

His face started into haggard lines; he lowered his eyes, and, with a short laugh, shook his head.

"Later; not now," he said. "You begin."

She laughed also. "I have seen Lord Hambleton," she said with a burst of excitement. "He is coming to-night." And watched upon his face for the effect.

"Oh, you clever girl!" he cried, his eyes smiling, his lips quivering slightly. "You clever girl."

Again she laughed. It almost seemed to her at that moment that she loved him.

"Ah, you would think so, if you knew how I managed it."

"But I know it, I know it," he cried, seizing her hand across the table. "You are as clever as you are beautiful."

He hardly recalled the point to which their conversation related; he was aware only of her proximity and her kindly eyes. She returned

returned the pressure of his fingers faintly, and looked at him thoughtfully.

"You look tired, Freddy," she said. "I'm afraid you've had a very wearisome day."

"Yes," he assented with a tiny laugh. "I háve had a bad day."

"Tell me," she said abruptly, "what about Maclagan?"

He rose. "Come into the study, then," he said in another voice. "I can tell you better there."

She followed him, laying a hand lightly upon his shoulder. She took her seat within the comfortable armchair, stretching herself out, with her feet to the fire and the red light upon her face and bosom. Rosewarne leaned his elbow on the mantelpiece.

"Well?" she asked presently in a tone of invitation.

He started. "Dolly," he said slowly, "supposing I were—to die—would you——"

"Good gracious, Freddy, don't talk nonsense," she interrupted on his halting phrases. "We haven't come to talk about foolish things like that."

He made no answer, but stared harder into the fire. A sense of irritation grew upon Mrs. Rosewarne. Had he failed in his mission. If he had, at least she had succeeded in hers, and the thought consoled her.

"Now, let me hear all about it. Do be quick," she said.

He turned to her suddenly. "Dolly, you must answer me; please answer me," he cried in agitation. "You could not bear my death, could you? Say you couldn't."

"Of course not," she replied sharply. "Why in the name of all that is decent will you harp on that? Don't be morbid."

"It will have to come to that," he said brokenly.

"Pooh! Don't be foolish," she retorted. She regarded him critically.

critically. Even in the red light the colour of his face, which had fallen into ugly lines, repelled her. "Come, what is it? Is anything the matter with you? Have you seen your doctor? What are you keeping from me?"

The questions ran off her tongue sharply, even acrimoniously. She had anew the sense of irritation that he had chosen this hour to be ill.

"No," he replied in a blank voice, "I suppose I'm all right. I don't know. I've been—yes—I'm ill with the horrible trouble. I'm——" He fell quickly upon his knees, burying his face in her gown. "Oh, Dolly, Dolly," he sobbed, "I have ruined you, and you don't know it. It is all over—all over."

Her eyes opened in alarm, but she did not move. "What nonsense are you talking, Freddy?" she asked in an uncertain voice which rang harshly. "You're ill. You've been overworking. You mustn't. What foolishness!"

She laughed faintly, with embarrassment, and almost mechanically put out a hand and touched his hair as though vaguely to reassure him of his mistake; while all the time her heart thumped on and her mind was wondering in a daze.

At her touch he raised his head, and clutched her, crying, "Ah, you do love me, Dolly. You do love me. I knew you loved me. I knew you would be sorry for me."

She sat motionless, fear reaching out arms for her heart. Slowly she was beginning to understand.

"What is it that you have done?" she asked in a dry voice.

He pressed her hand tightly, crushing her fingers. "I have taken money," he whispered, "trust money. I am ruined. I must go to prison, unless I——"

She moistened her lips, impassive as ever.

"But you do love me," he repeated, clinging to her. "Yes, you

you do love me, Dolly. Even if I have to do—that thing, you love me still."

Through all her being ran a repulsion for this creature at her knees, but she was clogged with her emotions and sat silent.

"Dolly, Dolly," he cried pathetically. "I shall have to do it. I know I shall have to do it—I——" He looked up, gulping down his sobs, as though seeking in her face for a contradiction. He knew the warm tears would fall upon him. Through his blurred vision he saw her mutely, indistinctly, raise her arms, extracting her hand from his grasp. He felt—he knew—he hoped—— Ah, she would throw them about his neck and draw him close in a passionate, pitiful embrace.

"Dolly, Dolly," he whispered, "I shall have to die."

With a rough movement she thrust him from her and got upon her feet.

"Die!" she exclaimed in a voice full of ineffable bitterness. "Die! Oh, my God, yes. That is the least you can do."

He lay where he had fallen to her push, huddled in a shapeless heap, stirring faintly. It was to her eyes as if some vermin upon which she had set her foot still moved with life. There was left in him no power of thought, no capacity of emotion. He was dimly conscious of misery, and he knew that she was standing by. Far away a tune sounded, and reverberated in his ears; it was the singing of the empty air. She was staring upon him with disgust and terror.

"Poor worm!" she said in tense low tones; and then her eyes alighted on her heaving bosom and the glories of her gown. The revulsion struck her like a blow, and she reeled under it. "You devil!" she cried. "You have ruined my life."

The sound of those sharp words smote upon his brain, and
whipped

whipped his ragged soul. He rose suddenly to his feet, his face blazing with fury.

"Damn you," he cried passionately. "I have loved you. I have sold my soul for you. I have ruined my mind for you. Damn you, Dorothy. And you have no words for me. Damn you."

His voice trailed away into a tremulous sob, and he stood contemplating her with fixed eyes. She laughed hardly, withdrawing her skirts from his vicinity. His gaze wandered from her, and went furtively towards the mantelpiece. She followed it, and saw a revolver lying upon the marble.

"Bah!" she said. "You have not the courage."

At that moment a knock fell upon the door; after a pause she moved and opened it.

"Lord Hambleton, ma'am," said Williams. "He is in the drawing-room."

Breathing hard, she looked round at her husband. Rosewarne's dull eyes were fixed upon her. They interceded with her; they fawned upon her.

"I will be there in a moment," she said clearly. Rosewarne moved slowly to the table and sat down, resting his head in his hands. He made no protest; if he realised anything now, he realised that he had expected this. The door shut to behind her; a dull pain started in the base of his brain; into the redoubts of his soul streamed swiftly the forces of sheer panic.

Mrs. Rosewarne entered the drawing-room, the tail of her dress rustling over the carpet. Lord Hambleton turned with this sound in his ears, stirring him pleasantly.

"Well," said he, smiling, "you see I've come."

She gave him her hand and paused, confronting him. Her heart thumped like a hammer upon her side; her face was flushed with colour, and her lips quivered.

"It

"It is good of you," she said tremulously ; "won't you sit down ? "

He did not heed her invitation, but shot a shrewd glance at her. Her voice startled him ; the discomposure of her appearance arrested his eyes. He wondered what had happened. It could not be that his visit was the cause of this confusion. And yet he noted it with a thrill of satisfaction, such as he had experienced in the colloquy at Mrs. Charters's.

"You are very good to look at like this," he allowed himself to say. He picked up the thread of their communion where it had been dropped earlier that day. She was marvellously handsome ; he had never admired a woman so much since his youth. The faint light spreading from the lamps illumined her brilliant face and threw up her figure in a kind of twilight against the wall.

Her heart palpitated audibly ; it seemed to her that she had a sudden unreasonable desire to laugh. The squalid gloom of that chamber beyond lifted ; it seemed remote and accidental. She was here with the comfortable eyes of this man upon her, contemplating her with admiration. She was not a parcel of that tragedy outside. She smiled broadly.

"Why, the better for my *salon*," she said.

What had excited her ? he asked himself. "Ah ! we will arrange all that," he answered with a familiar nod.

"You will ? " she asked eagerly—breathlessly.

"Why, certainly," he replied. "I think we can manage it— between us."

She laughed aloud this time. "Yes, both of us together," she said.

He met her eyes. Was it wine ? he asked. Or was it—— ? Lord Hambleton's body tingled with sensation. He had not suspected that matters had progressed so intimately between them. Almost

Almost involuntarily he put out a hand towards her. She laughed awkwardly, and he drew it back.

"You should have had it long ago," he said. "You have thrown away a chance."

"My life, you mean," she cried, breaking in upon his mellifluous tones with a harsher note.

She shifted her head towards the door as if listening for a sound. Her action struck him for the moment as ungainly.

"Things do not always fall out as we want them," he said slowly.

"Not as you want them?" she asked, coming back to regard him. "Why, what more do you want?"

He watched her from his quiet eyes, which suddenly lost their equable expression. To him she had always appeared a woman of dispassion, but now the seeming surrender in her mind, the revolution in her character, flashed upon him with an extreme sense of emotion. His heart beat faster.

"I think you know," he said softly, and reaching forth, took her hand.

Swiftly she turned; a look of dread rushed into her eyes. All on a sudden the transactions of that neighbouring room leapt into proximity. She saw Freddy handling the revolver; she watched him lean over the table and cock it in the light; she saw him—— She gave a cry, and moved a step towards the door, with a frightened face.

"What is it?" asked Lord Hambleton in alarm. "You are ill. You——" She made no answer, and he seized her hand again. "Let me ring for a glass of wine," he whispered.

Mrs. Rosewarne laughed loudly in his face.

"No, no," she said; "it is nothing. Pray, don't. I shall be better."

She

She looked at him, and then turned her ear to the door again, listening with a white face. He watched her anxiously, but in his own mind the reason of her perturbation was clear. The thought was sweet to him.

"Well," said he ; "and now to business."

"Business !" she echoed, and moved quickly to him, "I——Please, you must excuse me, Lord Hambleton. My husband is ill. Do you mind ? I——"

He rose abruptly. "I am very sorry," he said ; "I will not trouble you, then, just now."

He took his hat. She had turned away and was hearkening with all her senses for that report that did not come. He bit his lips. Perhaps she had been overstrained. He could scarce say what feeling ran uppermost in his mind. She hurried him to the door, accompanying him herself.

"Must you go ?" she asked, stupidly, on the doorstep.

He looked at her ; perhaps she really was ill. But she was very beautiful. She did not hear his answer. The rough wind blew through the open door and scattered her hair and her skirts. Lord Hambleton went down the steps. She watched him go. At that moment, somehow, a great revulsion overwhelmed her. She had listened, and there had been no discharge. What a fool she had been ! Of course, he had no courage. She had the desire to rush after Lord Hambleton and call him back. She had tortured herself idly ; she had played a silly part in a melodrama. She recalled Lord Hambleton's ardent gaze. There was a man ! Ah, if this thing were not fastened about her neck ! She stole back along the hall—furious. Once more she was confronted with the squalor of her position. Her indignation rose higher ; she could see that pitiful creature crying for mercy, crying for affection. Bah ! He was too cowardly to die. Burning with the old anger, she
                                                                crossed

crossed to the study and opened the door. She would have it out with him; they should understand their position. With Lord Hambleton the dignified prospects of her life had vanished, and she was flung back upon a mean and ignominious lot.

Rosewarne was seated in the armchair; the revolver rested where it had lain upon the mantelpiece. He made no movement to rise as she returned, and she stood for a second looking down upon him from behind with curling lips. A bottle of whisky and a glass stood upon the table at his elbow. It was probable that he had drunk himself to sleep.

"Are you awake?" she called sharply. He made no sign. She bent over angrily and shook him.

His head fell to her touch, and from his fingers a little phial tumbled upon the floor.

A Song

By Rosamund Marriott-Watson

Requiescat

Bury me deep when I am dead,
　Far from the woods where sweet birds sing;
Lap me in sullen stone and lead,
　Lest my poor dust should feel the spring.

Never a flower be near me set,
　Nor starry cup nor slender stem,
Anemone nor violet,
　Lest my poor dust remember them.

And you—wherever you may fare—
　Dearer than birds, or flowers, or dew—
Never, ah me, pass never there,
　Lest my poor dust should dream of you.

Six Drawings

By Aubrey Beardsley

I. Portrait of Himself

II. L'Education Sentimentale

III.Portrait of Mrs. Patrick Campbell

IV.The Repentance of Mrs. * * * *

V. The Comedy-Ballet of Marionnettes,
as performed by the troupe of the
Théâtre Impossible.

VI. La Dame aux Camélias

PAR LES DIEVX
JVMEAVX TOVS
LES MONSTRES
NE SONT PAS EN
AFRIQVE.

THE REPENTANCE
OF Mrs . . . .

Tree-Worship

By Richard Le Gallienne

Vast and mysterious brother, ere was yet of me
  So much as men may poise upon a needle's end,
Still shook with laughter all this monstrous might of thee,
  And still with haughty crest it called the morning friend.

Thy latticed column jetted up the bright blue air,
  Tall as a mast it was, and stronger than a tower ;
Three hundred winters had beheld thee mighty there,
  Before my little life had lived one little hour.

With rocky foot stern-set like iron in the land,
  With leafy rustling crest the morning sows with pearls,
Huge as a minster, half in heaven men saw thee stand,
  Thy rugged girth the waists of fifty Eastern girls.

Knotted and warted, slabbed and armoured like the hide
  Of tropic elephant ; unstormable and steep
As some grim fortress with a princess-pearl inside,
  Where savage guardian faces beard the bastioned keep :

So

So hard a rind, old tree, shielding so soft a heart,
    A woman's heart of tender little nestling leaves ;
Nor rind so hard but that a touch so soft can part,
    And spring's first baby-bud an easy passage cleaves.

I picture thee within with dainty satin sides,
    Where all the long day through the sleeping dryad dreams,
But when the moon bends low and taps thee thrice she glides,
    Knowing the fairy knock, to bask within her beams.

And all the long night through, for him with eyes and ears,
    She sways within thine arms and sings a fairy tune,
Till, startled with the dawn, she softly disappears,
    And sleeps and dreams again until the rising moon.

But with the peep of day great bands of heavenly birds
    Fill all thy branchy chambers with a thousand flutes,
And with the torrid noon stroll up the weary herds,
    To seek thy friendly shade and doze about thy roots ;

Till with the setting sun they turn them once more home :
    And, ere the moon dawns, for a brief enchanted space,
Weary with million miles, the sore-spent star-beams come,
    And moths and bats hold witches' sabbath in the place.

And then I picture thee some bloodstained Holyrood,
    Dread haunted palace of the bat and owl, whence steal,
Shrouded all day, lost murdered spirits of the wood,
    And fright young happy nests with homeless hoot and
        squeal.

                                        Some

By Richard Le Gallienne

Some Rizzio nightingale that plained adulterous love
   Beneath the boudoir-bough of some fast-married bird,
Some dove that cooed to some one else's lawful dove,
   And felt the dagger-beak pierce while his lady heard.

Then, maybe, dangling from thy gloomy gallows boughs,
   A human corpse swings, mournful, rattling bones and
      chains—
His eighteenth century flesh hath fattened nineteenth century
      cows—
   Ghastly Æolian harp fingered of winds and rains.

Poor Rizpah comes to reap each newly-fallen bone
   That once thrilled soft, a little limb, within her womb ;
And mark yon alchemist, with zodiac-spangled zone,
   Wrenching the mandrake root that fattens in the gloom.

So rounds thy day, from maiden morn to haunted night,
   From larks and sunlit dreams to owl and gibbering ghost ;
A catacomb of dark, a sponge of living light,
   To the wide sea of air a green and welcome coast.

I seek a god, old tree : accept my worship, thou !
   All other gods have failed me always in my need.
I hang my votive song beneath thy temple bough,
   Unto thy strength I cry—Old monster, be my creed !

Give me to clasp this earth with feeding roots like thine,
   To mount yon heaven with such star-aspiring head,
Fill full with sap and buds this shrunken life of mine,
   And from my boughs O might such stalwart sons be shed !
                            With

With loving cheek pressed close against thy horny breast,
    I hear the roar of sap mounting within thy veins ;
Tingling with buds, thy great hands open towards the west,
    To catch the sweetheart wind that brings the sister rains.

O winds that blow from out the fruitful mouth of God,
    O rains that softly fall from his all-loving eyes,
You that bring buds to trees and daisies to the sod,
    O God's best Angel of the Spring, in me arise.

Suggestion

By Mrs. Ernest Leverson

I F Lady Winthrop had not spoken of me as " that intolerable, effeminate boy," she might have had some chance of marrying my father. She was a middle-aged widow; prosaic, fond of domineering, and an alarmingly excellent housekeeper; the serious work of her life was paying visits; in her lighter moments she collected autographs. She was highly suitable and altogether insupportable; and this unfortunate remark about me was, as people say, the last straw. Some encouragement from father Lady Winthrop must, I think, have received; for she took to calling at odd hours, asking my sister Marjorie sudden abrupt questions, and being generally impossible. A tradition existed that her advice was of use to our father in his household, and when, last year, he married his daughter's school-friend, a beautiful girl of twenty, it surprised every one except Marjorie and myself.

The whole thing was done, in fact, by suggestion. I shall never forget that summer evening when father first realised, with regard to Laura Egerton, the possible. He was giving a little dinner of eighteen people. *Through a mistake of Marjorie's* (my idea) Lady Winthrop did not receive her invitation till the very last minute. Of course she accepted—we knew she would—but unknowing that it was a dinner party, she came without putting on evening-dress.

Nothing

Nothing could be more trying to the average woman than such a *contretemps ;* and Lady Winthrop was not one to rise, sublimely, and laughing, above the situation. I can see her now, in a plaid blouse and a vile temper, displaying herself, mentally and physically, to the utmost disadvantage, while Marjorie apologised the whole evening, in pale blue crèpe-de-chine ; and Laura, in yellow, with mauve orchids, sat—an adorable contrast—on my father's other side, with a slightly conscious air that was perfectly fascinating. It is quite extraordinary what trifles have their little effect in these matters. *I* had sent Laura the orchids, anonymously ; I could not help it if she chose to think they were from my father. Also, I had hinted of his secret affection for her, and lent her Verlaine. I said I had found it in his study, turned down at her favourite page. Laura has, like myself, the artistic temperament ; she is cultured, rather romantic, and in search of the *au-delà*. My father has at times—never to me—rather charming manners ; also he is still handsome, with that look of having suffered that comes from enjoying oneself too much. That evening his really sham melancholy and apparently hollow gaiety were delightful for a son to witness, and appealed evidently to her heart. Yes, strange as it may seem, while the world said that pretty Miss Egerton married old Carington for his money, she was really in love, or thought herself in love, with our father. Poor girl ! She little knew what an irritating, ill-tempered, absent-minded person he is in private life ; and at times I have pangs of remorse.

A fortnight after the wedding, father forgot he was married, and began again treating Laura with a sort of *distrait* gallantry as Marjorie's friend, or else ignoring her altogether. When, from time to time, he remembers she is his wife, he scolds her about the housekeeping in a fitful, perfunctory way, for he does not know that Marjorie does it still. Laura bears the rebukes like an angel ;
indeed,

indeed, rather than take the slightest practical trouble she would prefer to listen to the strongest language in my father's vocabulary.

But she is sensitive; and when father, speedily resuming his bachelor manners, recommenced his visits to an old friend who lives in one of the little houses opposite the Oratory, she seemed quite vexed. Father is horribly careless, and Laura found a letter. They had a rather serious explanation, and for a little time after, Laura seemed depressed. She soon tried to rouse herself, and is at times cheerful enough with Marjorie and myself, but I fear she has had a disillusion. They never quarrel now, and I think we all three dislike father about equally, though Laura never owns it, and is gracefully attentive to him in a gentle, filial sort of way.

We are fond of going to parties—not father—and Laura is a very nice chaperone for Marjorie. They are both perfectly devoted to me. "Cecil knows everything," they are always saying, and they do nothing—not even choosing a hat—without asking my advice.

Since I left Eton I am supposed to be reading with a tutor, but as a matter of fact I have plenty of leisure; and am very glad to be of use to the girls, of whom I'm, by the way, quite proud. They are rather a sweet contrast; Marjorie has the sort of fresh rosy prettiness you see in the park and on the river. She is tall, and slim as a punt-pole, and if she were not very careful how she dresses, she would look like a drawing by Pilotelle in the *Lady's Pictorial*. She is practical and lively, she rides and drives and dances; skates, and goes to some mysterious haunt called *The Stores*, and is, in her own way, quite a modern English type.

Laura has that exotic beauty so much admired by Philistines; dreamy dark eyes, and a wonderful white complexion. She loves

music

music and poetry and pictures and admiration in a lofty sort of way; she has a morbid fondness for mental gymnastics, and a dislike to physical exertion, and never takes any exercise except waving her hair. Sometimes she looks bored, and I have heard her sigh.

"Cissy," Marjorie said, coming one day into my study, "I want to speak to you about Laura."

"Do you have pangs of conscience too?" I asked, lighting a cigarette.

"Dear, we took a great responsibility. Poor girl! Oh, couldn't we make Papa more——"

"Impossible," I said; "no one has any influence with him. He can't bear even me, though if he had a shade of decency he would dash away an unbidden tear every time I look at him with my mother's blue eyes."

My poor mother was a great beauty, and I am supposed to be her living image.

"Laura has no object in life," said Marjorie. "I have, all girls have, I suppose. By the way, Cissy, I am quite sure Charlie Winthrop is serious."

"How sweet of him! I am so glad. I got father off my hands last season."

"Must I really marry him, Cissy? He bores me."

"What has that to do with it? Certainly you must. You are not a beauty, and I doubt your ever having a better chance."

Marjorie rose and looked at herself in the long pier-glass that stands opposite my writing-table. I could not resist the temptation to go and stand beside her.

"I am just the style that is admired now," said Marjorie, dispassionately.

"So

" So am I," I said reflectively. " But *you* will soon be out of date."

Every one says I am strangely like my mother. Her face was of that pure and perfect oval one so seldom sees, with delicate features, rosebud mouth, and soft flaxen hair. A blondness without insipidity, for the dark-blue eyes are fringed with dark lashes, and from their languorous depths looks out a soft mockery. I have a curious ideal devotion to my mother; she died when I was quite young—only two months old—and I often spend hours thinking of her, as I gaze at myself in the mirror.

" Do come down from the clouds," said Marjorie impatiently, for I had sunk into a reverie. " I came to ask you to think of something to amuse Laura—to interest her."

" We ought to make it up to her in some way. Haven't you tried anything? "

" Only palmistry; and Mrs. Wilkinson prophesied her all that she detests, and depressed her dreadfully."

" What do you think she really needs most? " I asked.

Our eyes met.

" Really, Cissy, you're too disgraceful," said Marjorie. There was a pause.

" And so I'm to accept Charlie? "

" What man do you like better? " I asked.

" I don't know what you mean," said Marjorie, colouring.

" *I* thought Adrian Grant would have been more sympathetic to Laura than to you. I have just had a note from him, asking me to tea at his studio to-day." I threw it to her. " He says I'm to bring you both. Would that amuse Laura? "

" Oh," cried Marjorie, enchanted, " of course we'll go. I wonder what he thinks of me," she added wistfully.

" He didn't say. He is going to send Laura his verses, 'Hearts-ease and Heliotrope.' "

She

She sighed. Then she said, " Father was complaining again to-day of your laziness."

" I, lazy ! Why, I've been swinging the censer in Laura's boudoir because she wants to encourage the religious temperament, and I've designed your dress for the Clives' fancy ball."

" Where's the design ? "

" In my head. You're not to wear white ; Miss Clive must wear white."

" I wonder you don't marry her," said Marjorie, " you admire her so much."

" I never marry. Besides, I know she's pretty, but that furtive Slade-school manner of hers gets on my nerves. You don't know how dreadfully I suffer from my nerves."

She lingered a little, asking me what I advised her to choose for a birthday present for herself—an American organ, a black poodle, or an *édition de luxe* of Browning. I advised the last, as being least noisy. Then I told her I felt sure that in spite of her admiration for Adrian, she was far too good natured to interfere with Laura's prospects. She said I was incorrigible, and left the room with a smile of resignation.

And I returned to my reading. On my last birthday—I was seventeen—my father—who has his gleams of dry humour— gave me *Robinson Crusoe !* I prefer Pierre Loti, and intend to have an onyx-paved bath-room, with soft apricot-coloured light shimmering through the blue-lined green curtains in my chambers, as soon as I get Margery married, and Laura more—settled down.

I met Adrian Grant first at a luncheon party at the Clives . I seemed to amuse him ; he came to see me, and became at once obviously enamoured of my step-mother. He is rather an impressionable impressionist, and a delightful creature, tall and graceful and beautiful, and altogether most interesting. Every one
admits

admits he's fascinating; he is very popular and very much disliked. He is by way of being a painter; he has a little money of his own —enough for his telegrams, but not enough for his buttonholes— and nothing could be more incongruous than the idea of his marrying. I have never seen Marjorie so much attracted. But she is a good loyal girl, and will accept Charlie Winthrop, who is a dear person, good-natured and ridiculously rich—just the sort of man for a brother-in-law. It will annoy my old enemy Lady Winthrop—he is her nephew, and she wants him to marry that little Miss Clive. Dorothy Clive has her failings, but she could not—to do her justice—be happy with Charlie Winthrop.

Adrian's gorgeous studio gives one the complex impression of being at once the calm retreat of a mediæval saint and the luxurious abode of a modern Pagan. One feels that everything could be done there, everything from praying to flirting—everything except painting. The tea-party amused me, I was pretending to listen to a brown person who was talking absurd worn-out literary clichés— as that the New Humour is not funny, or that Bourget understood women, when I overheard this fragment of conversation.

"But don't you like Society?" Adrian was saying.

"I get rather tired of it. People are so much alike. They all say the same things," said Laura.

"Of course they all say the same things to *you*," murmured Adrian, as he affected to point out a rather curious old silver crucifix.

"That," said Laura, "is one of the things they say."

* * * * *

About three weeks later I found myself dining alone with Adrian Grant, at one of the two restaurants in London. (The cooking is better at the other, this one is the more becoming.) I had lilies-of-the-valley in my button-hole, Adrian was wearing a

red

red carnation. Several people glanced at us. Of course he is very well known in Society. Also, I was looking rather nice, and I could not help hoping, while Adrian gazed rather absently over my head, that the shaded candles were staining to a richer rose the waking wonder of my face.

Adrian was charming of course, but he seemed worried and a little preoccupied, and drank a good deal of champagne.

Towards the end of dinner, he said—almost abruptly for him—" Carington."

" Cecil," I interrupted. He smiled.

" Cissy . . . it seems an odd thing to say to you, but though you are so young, I think you know everything. I am sure you know everything. You know about me. I am in love. I am quite miserable. What on earth am I to do ! " He drank more champagne. " Tell me," he said, " what to do." For a few minutes, while we listened to that interminable hackneyed *Intermezzo*, I reflected ; asking myself by what strange phases I had risen to the extraordinary position of giving advice to Adrian on such a subject ?

Laura was not happy with our father. From a selfish motive, Marjorie and I had practically arranged that monstrous marriage. That very day he had been disagreeable, asking me with a clumsy sarcasm to raise his allowance, so that he could afford my favourite cigarettes. If Adrian were free, Marjorie might refuse Charlie Winthrop. I don't want her to refuse him. Adrian has treated me as a friend. I like him—I like him enormously. I am quite devoted to him. And how can I rid myself of the feeling of responsibility, the sense that I owe some compensation to poor beautiful Laura ?

We spoke of various matters. Just before we left the table, I said, with what seemed, but was not, irrelevance, " Dear Adrian, Mrs. Carington——"

" Go

" Go on, Cissy."

" She is one of those who must be appealed to, at first, by her imagination. She married our father because she thought he was lonely and misunderstood."

" *I* am lonely and misunderstood," said Adrian, his eyes flashing with delight.

" Ah, not twice ! She doesn't like that now."

I finished my coffee slowly, and then I said,

" Go to the Clives' fancy-ball as Tristan."

Adrian pressed my hand. . . .

At the door of the restaurant we parted, and I drove home through the cool April night, wondering, wondering. Suddenly I thought of my mother—my beautiful sainted mother, who would have loved me, I am convinced, had she lived, with an extraordinary devotion. What would she have said to all this ? What would she have thought ? I know not why, but a mad reaction seized me. I felt recklessly conscientious. My father ! After all, he was my father. I was possessed by passionate scruples. If I went back now to Adrian—if I went back and implored him, supplicated him never to see Laura again !

I felt I could persuade him. I have sufficient personal magnetism to do that, if I make up my mind. After one glance in the looking-glass, I put up my stick and stopped the hansom. I had taken a resolution. I told the man to drive to Adrian's rooms.

He turned round with a sharp jerk. In another second a brougham passed us—a swift little brougham that I knew. It slackened—it stopped—we passed it—I saw my father. He was getting out at one of the little houses opposite the Brompton Oratory.

" Turn round again," I shouted to the cabman. And he drove me straight home.

Two Pictures

By Walter Sickert

Lucretia

By K. Douglas King

I

I n his life John Burnett suffered no distinction in any circles beyond that immediate one of his acquaintances and friends. He was an insignificant man in appearance, in moral force, in intellect, and in rank—which was that of a navvy. Such fame as was his in Eastown-by-Line (the mushroom town wherein he lived, and on whose railroads he worked) came solely through his domestic troubles. Naturally, the source of these troubles was a woman ; his wife, Lucretia—Luce, for short.

So far as looks went there could not have been a worse assorted couple than the navvy and his wife. Luce was a splendidly formed woman, with straight features, level brows, and a penetrating way of looking out of a pair of very handsome eyes ; but with a screw loose somewhere in the complex machinery of her moral being. This was the reason why her mouth, which should have been large and generous, to match her eyes, was curved to a foolish, little droop, at the corners ; and why her lips, when they were not giving vent to absurd and impossible aspirations, were pursed up in a thin martyr-shape.

She had a twin sister, who hardly belongs to this story, but
who

who told her once that this martyr-expression completely spoilt her natural good looks. Luce did not discontinue to assume it, even then.

She was a good workwoman, and had been employed as a forewoman in a large dressmaking establishment, before John Burnett (as much to his own as to others' astonishment) carried her off as his wife to Eastown-by-Line. Her married life (including the bearing of Burnett's children, the rearing of them, and looking after her husband and the house) entailed on her sufficient work to keep her mind, as well as body, fully occupied from sunrise to midnight. In the pursuance of her wifely and motherly duties she allowed her mind to run woefully astray. That was the fatal crook in her soul ; and, in consequence, her husband's dinners, the home comfort, and the six Burnett children (who were a disgrace to their town, so ill-kept were their persons) suffered severely. If she had been " born a lady " she would have read " advanced " books, and become an " advanced " woman. Also, she would have refused the John Burnetts of her own station who sought her hand in marriage. She would have known she had a higher duty to perform than to marry a mere man, and would have acted, generally, according to her convictions —which were of a subjective nature.

As she had neither the leisure nor the means wherewith to cultivate the abnormal in her soul, she asserted her independent womanhood by an intrigue with another man. This other man lived alone, in a large, ugly ten-roomed villa, part of whose garden wall formed the eastern boundary of the Burnett backyard. The navvy lived in the last of a tiny, frail row of four-roomed houses, on the outskirts of central Eastown-by-Line. The name of their street was Aspect Road, most felicitously named since it overlooked a brickfield at its upper end and the gasworks at
the

the lower. The new line in course of construction ran, in an animated streak, between this " view " and Aspect Road, which was separated from the railway by a low, sloping bank. The Burnett children, from behind their front garden hedge, used to throw stones at their father and his mates working on the line, so short was the distance from the houses to the railroad. The eastern part of the town was composed of villas and small shops, and one long, straight avenue, lined with chestnut-trees. There were six of these trees on either side of the street, and they were the only trees in the town, except two others—also chestnuts—in the other man's garden. From west to east, and from the canal on the south to the railroad on the north, the entire town was a ghastly blot on the face of the earth.

Life's ironical ruling ordained that the other man should be the assistant superintending engineer of that part of the line on whose construction Burnett was engaged. His name was Caldwell, and he first saw Luce when she was airing the Burnett linen on her little line that stretched across the whole area of her back-yard.

Luce's manner whilst hanging out the clothes, that memorable day, was fraught with a mixture of indolence (which was characteristic) and impatience, born of intense distaste for the work in hand. It received presentment in her languid movements and smouldering eyes. She had been at work since five in the morning, and it was now six in the evening, and she had still five more hours' work before her. Of course the woman was tired in body and sick in soul. It never entered John Burnett's mind (he being a man, and a mediocre one at that) that the commonplace drudgery of existence is sheer bondage to the woman who has sufficient imagination to realise freedom, but not enough to idealise duty ; and whose household tasks, commencing at

marriage

marriage and ending with death, imprison her from dawn to dusk within four tiny walls.

Luce was in a tense state, and only a match was needed to set a volcano ablaze. Caldwell watched her as she moved from line to basket and back again, her fine eyes alight with unsatisfied desire; her thin lips pouting; a tired flush on her curved cheeks; her hair falling untidily over her handsome, heavy brow. Watching her, the assistant superintendent coveted her.

It was not Caldwell's habit to lose time in advancing towards the attainment of his desires. Between the first attack and the first conditional surrender, the flame of that desire spread and intensified until it became a passion that penetrated to the deepest recesses of his being. Luce was in the most dangerous state of mind that a woman can possibly be in. She wanted something. She did not know what she wanted. Moreover, she did not care any longer about the opinions of her little world. This recklessness of mood brings shipwreck in its train more surely than the most deliberately planned wrongdoing. The first advances came from Caldwell. Luce responded to them with such doubtful eyes and such a passionately wistful mouth that the assistant superintendent, connoisseur as he was in his way, lost his head. He recovered it almost immediately; but then the mischief was done.

Burnett had broad, stunted features, a slouching bearing, deeply sunken, almost invisible eyes, a slow-moving intellect, and no social or conversational gifts whatever. Caldwell, on the contrary, was a fluent talker, and as flashy in intellect as in appearance. His prominent lips were shaded by a handsome moustache, and his eyes were bold, blue and bright. Also, he was a fine, tall fellow, and, without conceit, could lay claim to a knowledge of women and their inscrutable ways above that of the average man. This

was

was almost as powerful a factor in his success as Luce's own unfortunate mood. Such love as she had ever felt for John Burnett was already worn thin by interminable toil for him, his house, and his children.

When a woman speaks of her offspring as " his children " one of two things is in process. Either she is meditating a desperate leap into the dark, or she is digesting the discovery of a new, hitherto undreamt-of virtue in her husband. Now Burnett had no special virtues whatever ; at least, such as Luce could appreciate. When she began to think of the children as " his children," she was already far on the road that leads to dishonour.

That evening when she hung out her washing, and Caldwell had first seen her, was one far advanced in April. It was now late in May, and Scandal was very loud and busy up Aspect Road. Tremulous-mouthed Lucretia did not care. She was living a double existence, and Burnett and the children had only the hollow crust of her attentions. After the first resistance, Caldwell did not find it difficult to persuade her that Desire was Duty differently spelt, and that her present duty was to minister to his. A strong man, or a very selfish man, might have saved Luce yet. But Burnett was neither strong nor selfish. He loved his wife and was fond of his children ; but was as weak in the management of one as of the other.

He submitted to his home discomfort like a lamb, instead of roaring like a lion when half-raw or burnt-up food was set before him. Of course, this complaisance completed the woman's demoralisation ; just as much as his easy-going, indulgent ways with his children caused them to develop into veritable demons of juvenile wickedness. When he first heard from the neighbours' idle talk that his wife was going wrong with another man, and that man was his own superintendent, he simply did not believe it,

and

and went his daily ways without care or perturbation. He loved his wife, and he still believed in her honesty, although he was aware, at last, after ten years' vain delusion, that she was no cook.

Scandal, as usual, was premature in its assertions. It spoke as early as April, while May had passed before Lucretia really fell. It was on the third of June that Caldwell had said to her, as she stood by her cottage door, shading her lovely, sad, wild eyes from the setting sun : " Lucy, are you going to be cruel, still ? "

The assistant superintendent had just left the line and was going to his temporary villa home. His way home always took him past Burnett's cottage. For weeks past he had not ceased urging the woman to sin ; and last night she had faltered out to him, when he upbraided her, bitterly, for her cruel coquetry, that " To-morrow—perhaps—she would—do—what—he wished."

Against the sunset, his eyes flashing inquiry, reproach, and expectation upon her, he appeared as the representation of all manly and persuasive power. Luce changed colour, and her eyes dropped. Her eldest little daughter, Molly, standing by her side, glanced at the man with calm, splendid eyes of cold disfavour. She was neither fascinated by his glittering personality nor over-awed by his position.

Caldwell struck his foot, impatiently, on the ground. " Well, Luce ? " he cried, his eyes burning through her lowered eyelids, into her very soul ; his whole attitude a fierce interrogation. " Well, Luce ? "

Mrs. Burnett raised her eyes, quickly. They were unnaturally large and bright, and her face was very pale. She nodded, once or twice, and then turned round, hastily, and went indoors. Caldwell laughed ; a slight flush rose to his cheeks.

His fiery, amorous eyes, travelling back from the sharply closed door, rested, one second, on Molly Burnett, as she continued to

lean

lean against the gatepost, apparently unconscious of her surroundings. Molly detested Caldwell. It was this lovely, dirty, picturesque child who used to set her small brothers and sisters, armed with stones and dirt, on the assistant superintendent. Tiny arms and the strict necessity of cloaking their tactics by a stout hedge made the stones of no effect. Molly had the supreme pleasure, once, of seeing a piece of mud, aimed by her with feminine precision, stick to the back of his coat. She tried to bully her little brother, " Jack Spratt " Burnett, into piping rude remarks at him when they used to go down to the line, with the other East-town children, to watch operations there. To these heroic heights, however, Jack Spratt could not ascend. He had the pacific spirit ; and when Molly called him a " bloomin' sheep," neither resented the slur on his manhood with retort nor sought to efface it by action.

Molly's large shining eyes were fixed on the crimson cloudland on the northern horizon. She looked inexpressibly lovely. Caldwell shot a keener glance at her.

" Good-night, Molly," he called down, to the slim, motionless, little figure.

Mrs. Burnett's nine-year-old daughter stonily turned her eyes upon the man. There was a magnificent disdain in their pellucid depths. She raised her shoulders ever so slightly ; beyond the cold movement and that colder stare she made no response.

" By Jove ! " muttered Caldwell, genuine admiration leaping hotly out of his eyes. " What a lovely woman the hussy will be in ten years' time ! "

With a gay laugh, he bent forward, of a sudden, and thrust his moustached lips upon Molly's. Although she was taken completely by surprise, her defensive action was swifter than his attack. She ducked, and his mouth barely avoided sharp contact

with

with the top of the gatepost. The next second Molly had sprung up and struck him a resounding blow on the face.

Man as he was, Caldwell staggered back. Molly's eyes flashed fire from the other side of the gate. Her bosom heaved.

"Well, I'm damned!" gasped Caldwell at last, with a not unkindly laugh. "You—little vixen!"

He did not attempt to repeat the experiment, but applied his handkerchief to his cheek, where a red mark showed. Fortunately for the dignity of the assistant superintendent's reputation, both the thickness of the hedge and the sunset hour, when most of the workmen had gone home, had deprived the scene of spectators.

"Don't you think you can kiss everybody!" cried Molly, in a choked, passionate whisper, over the gate.

Molly had seen the assistant superintendent kiss her mother more than once. This action of his, and her mother's complete acquiescence therein, troubled her—though she could not have told why. It intensified her dislike of Caldwell into a positive loathing. She had told Jack Spratt he was to call the assistant superintendent a "toad" whenever he passed; and used to beat him when he tearfully refused.

Caldwell took off his hat, and made Molly a sweeping bow before he passed on.

"In five years, pretty Molly," he said, blandly, "I'll wager you won't refuse a man's kiss. You'll be as eager for kisses then, my girl, as any of 'em. They all are, you know, pretty Molly! There's not a petticoated creature made that isn't!"

"You're a lie," returned Molly, promptly. "You're a great, fat lie!"

Caldwell laughed again pleasantly, and turned on his heel. He was not angry, now that the first shock of his discomfiture was over; even though his cheek was still smartly stinging. When he he had swung his garden gate to behind him, he had forgotten all about his late misadventure. Lucretia's splendid eyes, with their vague longing and alternate melancholy and fire, possessed his vision. The exultation caused by her promise burned up again in his soul. He had made communication both easy and secret between the two households; the last barrier was broken down between them.

II

Burnett's domestic troubles were the common talk of Aspect Road. The matrons loudly expressed their disgust with Luce's share in the scandal. They reserved an opinion on the superintendent's part until the doors were closed. The husbands of most were working under Caldwell and his chief. The men on the line blamed Burnett for being a fool more than they condemned the assistant superintendent, in their hearts, for a knave. Though they gossiped freely among themselves, they forbore to offer any opinion on the case to Burnett himself. The women were not so considerate. Burnett's behaviour in allowing Luce (whose guilt was established beyond a doubt) to continue to live in his house, as if the sanctity of their marriage tie had never been violated, exasperated the women into shrill taunts, which were fearlessly and freely hurled at the unfortunate navvy.

Caldwell was not prepared at first that Lucretia should live entirely in his house; and Burnett, when the truth of the matter was at last borne in upon his stubborn, unreceptive brain, received from this fact some sort of faint comfort in the midst of his misery. His love for his wife was of unsuspected magnitude, and of a magnanimity beyond chivalry. It was not only for the sake of the six lovely, dirty little children who rioted, now without shadow

of

of restraint, about the road, that he was still willing to forgive Luce, and that he hoped against hope to win her back to him.

Luce went about her daily duties with little outward change. Perhaps there was more of dreamy haphazard in her method of work than before Caldwell came to possess her thoughts ; but there had been always so much left to Providence in the internal ordering of the Burnett household, that a little additional disorder was hardly noticeable. She grew to look more like a restless, untamed spirit every day. By turns she was passionately attentive to the children and completely neglectful of them. But her manner with them was always kind. Burnett, swayed by the twin spirits of his steadfast hope and his great affection, met her indifference to him with a phlegm that concealed, almost too successfully, the deadly wound her conduct was inflicting.

It was on June the third that Luce gave her fatal promise. The month of roses was drawing to an end before the navvy spoke to his wife of what lay up heavily on the hearts of each. Mrs. Burnett was lazily stirring porridge for the children's supper before the kitchen fire. Burnett had come in from work on the line two hours before. Ever since his entrance he had been watching her flitting dreamily to and fro—he moodily sitting in a corner, no word, good or bad, passing between the pair. It had been pay night, and it was one of the assistant superintendent's duties to pay the men their weekly wage. Burnett, whose innate sensitiveness was largely increased by the suspense and anguish of the last month, fancied Caldwell shot a look of triumph on him as he went up to receive his money at the superintendent's hand. As a matter of fact, Caldwell had done nothing of the sort. He hardly knew Burnett by sight, and he certainly did not wish to provoke Lucretia's husband into any manifestation of anger before the other men.

That

That fancied look, rankling in his heart, impelled the navvy at last to speak. But what he did and what he said were very different from that which he had intended to do or say.

"Oh, Luce, dear," he began, moving quickly forward and throwing his arms round the woman. "Oh, my dear, dear wife! Do come back to me, an' be as you was before this trouble began!"

Lucretia was thoroughly taken aback by this impetuous appeal, and by the violent exhibition of his feelings. The next minute, however, she rallied her forces, and slipped from his embrace. Turning, she faced him, with heightened colour and sparkling eyes. She held the spoon that she had hastily withdrawn from the saucepan when he had first seized her, and porridge dropped from it unheeded in great splashes on the floor.

"I—I haven't left you!" she cried, defiantly, the scarlet spot deepening in her cheeks. "And so how can I come back, pray?"

She cast a triumphant look on him, as if to ask how he thought he was going to answer that unanswerable question. Burnett's eyes were fixed on the largest porridge splash at his feet, and he only sighed heavily.

There was a short pause. Then Burnett in a hurried, stifled, voice:

"'Tis true—for all the same!"

"What's true?" asked the woman, with a toss of her head, and another flash of her eyes.

"What they're sayin' o' ye an'—an' that feller Caldwell," mumbled her husband. A savage glow lit up his downcast eyes one minute; the next, all the light was out, and they reassumed their normal dulness of appearance.

Mrs. Burnett made no reply, but resumed operations in her

porridge

porridge saucepan. The spoon clattered loudly against its metal sides, and Luce's hand trembled. Burnett shifted from one foot to the other. At last he burst out into speech again.

" I've never ill-treated ye, nor come home boozy, nor knocked the children about," said the navvy. " Ye've had my weekly wages reg'lar an' full always! and I've let ye go yer own way in the 'ouse an' never put in my oar in nothink, but let ye 'ave yer own way in everythink," he repeated, doggedly. " An' I can't think "—he choked—" I can't think why ye're treatin' me so ! "

Mrs. Burnett poured out porridge into six chipped plates. Her hands were shaking, and some of the scalding stuff splashed on to them. She bit her lips and spoke never a word.

" Lucy ! "

She started ; Burnett's voice was so soft and tremulous, and full of pleading love. Since the early days of their marriage, ten years ago, he had not called her anything but Luce. Now another man called her Lucy, whose voice was like music to her weary soul.

" Lucy," said Burnett, huskily, " oh, my girl, do come back, an'—an' love me as you used ! "

As his sad voice died away there came from without the sound of many little footsteps and voices. A look of extreme relief passed over the woman's face. The Burnett children, in spite of the irregular ways of the household, showed a remarkable genius for coming up to time, so far as the hours of the meals were concerned. The difficulty often was that they were ready for the meal before it was ready for them. Burnett slunk back to his corner at sound of their approach ; something like despair flitted across his stubbly, inexpressive face.

" You—you don't understand me ! " cried Mrs. Burnett, hurriedly,

hurriedly, over her shoulder, as her husband moved heavily away. There was the suspicion of a sob in her voice. " You never have understood me—never ! And talking of ill-treatment and all that shows you don't and can't understand me ! "

Burnett showed a face of blank, mystified despair at the eternal feminine wail. It was as incomprehensible to him as if it had been uttered in a foreign language of which he was entirely ignorant. It was the navvy's loss that Caldwell understood it as completely as man ever can.

The day after Burnett ventured his appeal, a momentous thing happened. It occurred at noon, and was nothing less than the breathless descent on the Burnett fold of Mrs. Burnett's twin sister.

Mrs. Burnett's sister was also a wife of ten years' experience ; but she was not a mother. It was her one bitter sorrow. Tidings of the Burnett-Caldwell scandal had reached her in her little Northamptonshire village, and her unexpected visit was the result. It occurred at the midday dinner hour, which, strange to say, was up to time that day. The Burnett flock were despatching slabs of suet pudding and treacle, carved and ladled out by Mrs. Burnett, at the kitchen dresser, when the cloaked and bonnetted apparition, omitting the formality of knocking, appeared in the doorway. Burnett was eating a solitary dinner on the bank overlooking the line in course of construction.

" Annie ! " cried Mrs. Burnett. She fell back a step ; her face, dyed suddenly scarlet at sight of her visitor, rapidly changed to a deadly pallor.

" Luce," said the other woman.

" Not before the children ! " cried Lucretia, putting out her hands, as if warding off a blow. " Oh, not a word before the children, Annie ! " she cried, passionately.

The

The other woman had Lucretia's splendid, slightly scornful eyes. Molly had her aunt's large, full mouth.

" I wasn't goin' to say a word," returned Annie ; her sad lips trembled. " 'Tisn't no use ; I knew that afore I came. I know you, Luce ! No ! an' I won't sit down an' eat anything, Luce ; I've a back train to catch, an' time's short. I came to ask, Luce, if——"

She faltered here, and changed colour. Lucretia bit her lips.

" Well," she said, sullenly, " if what ? "

" I came to ask if I could take the children home with me for a spell, Luce," said her sister, softly.

An indescribable tumult took possession of Lucretia's soul. Many conflicting voices clamoured for a hearing. Luce, confounded, taken by surprise, and dismayed to death at heart, listened with difficulty, to the loudest and most importunate.

" Yes," she said, heavily, at last ; " you can, if you like."

Mrs. Burnett's sister had come, primed with the best intentions in the world. She had not for a moment expected that her deliberately planned request would be granted. When Luce muttered out her slow " Yes," she was amazed, but not dismayed. She thought she was acting for the best in removing the Burnett children from the immediate scene of their mother's sin ; but the wisdom of her act may be questioned. In less than half an hour the entire flock was ready to start, baggage, such as it was, and all.

The parting was brief, and without undue expression of sentiment. The eleven months old baby was asleep when it changed hands. The childless woman received it with a most motherly caressing movement ; Luce's face was hard and rigid. The younger children were jubilant at the thought of the journey, but cried at having to leave their home, as they went down the little garden

garden path into the road. Jack Spratt neither cried nor laughed. He was awed by Molly's proud, pale face.

"Leave me—her," whispered Lucretia, with a little catch of her breath, and nodding, feverishly, in the direction of her eldest daughter, now occupied in nursing the youngest boy but one.

"God's sake not her—out of any of 'em!" cried back Molly's aunt, in a fierce, incoherent undertone; and Molly was swept off in the general exodus.

Mrs. Burnett watched them as they went down the dusty road. Molly carried the youngest baby, and her aunt had her late burden, a sturdy two-year-old. The two younger girls clasped hands, and walked demurely in front of the hen-in-charge. Jack Spratt walked alone, a few paces in front, as became the man of the party. Mrs. Burnett watched them, with dry eyes and burning eyeballs, until they were out of sight. Then she went indoors, and fell into a chair, sobbing and weeping, till her emotions seemed as if they would tear her thin frame asunder.

"Oh, if she had only left me Molly!" she moaned, in the intervals of her heavy sobbing. "If she had only left me my pretty Molly—my pretty, pretty girl!"

She had not recovered herself till four o'clock chimed out, unevenly, from the dilapidated kitchen clock. At that moment a man's footstep was heard to approach from without; and a man's voice called her name, softly, through the half-opened doorway.

He called her Lucy, and Mrs. Burnett leaped to her feet, and with a little, strangled cry, threw herself upon his breast. His arms met tightly round her, and he held her thus pressed to him, for a minute, without speaking. He could see her nerves were shattered, and that she was in a more desperate state even than when she had given him her first promise. "Oh, they've taken

away

away my children, Jamie ! " she sobbed out, at last. " Take me home with you ! don't leave me here in my empty home, Jamie ! I can't bear it ! "

Caldwell held her closer to him. He had come, fearing for once a possible refusal, on purpose to ask her that to which her own beseeching words to him now gave the affirmatory answer.

Five minutes later Luce left her home on his arm. " I'll take you right away from this one-horse place, Lucy," Caldwell said to her, as they went out. " My work is done here, with the doing of the line's."

He referred to the completion of the line, the last detail of whose construction would be an accomplished fact by sunset. With the running of the first train, thereon, on the morrow, Caldwell's duties, as assistant superintendent of the men at work on it, would be over.

" I'll belong to you now, Jamie, for ever and ever," Lucretia whispered up to him, as they gained his front door. She did not mind now if all the world saw her enter Caldwell's house. " They've taken my children away, and I'll only belong to you now, for ever and ever, Jamie," she repeated, as he led her into her new home. He bent and kissed her quivering lips.

When Burnett was going home that night, a neighbour, overflowing with news, darted out, from the next house. She had been waiting three hours for his advent, although she knew he could not be due in Aspect Road till past six. She was consumed with fear lest another neighbour should tell him the news before she had the chance.

She followed Burnett up his garden plot, in order to drive the bits of information deeper down into his dull, clouded brain.

" Their aunt came, Burnett, sure as I'm a livin' woman, and took 'em all away—the baby an' that limb, Molly, herself ! "
reiterated

reiterated the shrill-voiced informant. "How you stare, man! I tell you they're gone, the whole lot o' them; at half-past one they went past our windys, and says I, ' Lawks, that's Burnett's lot!'"

Burnett turned on his threshold and faced her with working jaws. She was not overcome at sight of his distress. Her mind flew off on a fresh tangent.

"An' Caldwell took *her* off, Burnett," went on the shrill tale-bearer. "In bare daylight, as bold as brass, she went off on his arm! these eyes o' mine saw it! 'twas like a theayter piece! and thinks I, oh, that poor soul, Burnett, who——"

The navvy waved her back, and she retired, somewhat awed at last, by his expression and his speechlessness. Burnett entered his empty home.

"I don't believe her," he muttered, staring vacantly around. "It's a damned lie!"

Nevertheless, the rooms were empty of wife, of children, and of children's clothes and broken toys. Burnett fell to thinking that perhaps the neighbour had not lied, after all.

A headless rag doll, lying under a chair, caught his eye. He remembered, with the first thrill of pain, recognised as such, that he had left his baby sucking it, contentedly, in its cradle when he went out that morning to put the finishing touches to the line. He stooped and picked it up, and stood, stroking it, mechanically, with his grimy hand. Burnett had not an ounce of sentiment about him, though he had a greater capacity for affection than Luce had ever discovered. After a while he ceased stroking the headless doll, and put it in his breast-pocket. He was not an heroic figure, in his far from clean working suit, and with his broad, undeveloped features and stubbly hair and beard; but, as he awkwardly shovelled the rag doll to his breast, his lower lip
trembling

Lucretia

trembling the while, he seemed to be invested with a pathetic majesty that was far above any physical grandeur.

"The childern's gone," thought Burnett, rousing himself with a heavy sigh. "But their aunt 'ull take care of 'em till—till the home's ready for 'em ag'in."

He went out, swiftly closing the door behind him. Twilight was falling, and a sense of great loneliness caught him for the first time, as if two hands had clutched him by the throat. He wheeled sharply towards Caldwell's house.

"She must come back if she thinks o' the childern, and knows I'm mor'n willing to have her back ag'in," he said to himself with a tearless sob. "She must do that!"

A bell hung to his hand by Caldwell's front door, and he pulled it. Though he was quite calm and composed to all outward appearances, he was, in reality, labouring under a violent excitement that made him feel sick and giddy. There was no response of any kind to his ring, and his eye caught the knocker on the door. He wondered, dully, why he had not seen it before, and struck it loudly several times on the metal plate.

There was a dreadful silence. Burnett's throat contracted. Then there came the sound of footsteps, and Caldwell himself threw the door open. He did not recognise his visitor at first, and met him with an impatient exclamation.

Burnett moved doggedly forward over the threshold, and a hanging lamp in the hall revealed his identity. Caldwell gave vent to a little low whistle of astonishment.

"I—I want to see my wife," stammered the navvy. He found it difficult to speak, owing to the dry condition of his lips. As Caldwell continued to preserve silence, he cried again, striking his nailed boot sharply on the hall floor, "I tell you I want to see the woman who's my wife!"

"Oh,

"Oh, come in, come in," said the assistant superintendent, blandly. "Only no violence before the lady, you know, and no threats."

"I'm not such a fool as to threaten," cried out Burnett, shaking from head to foot in his violent excitement. "I know I'm a fool and can't understand women like her," he added, bitterly. "But I'm not such a fool as to threaten her or any woman!"

"Oh, come in," repeated Caldwell, opening a door at the end of the passage. He passed in himself, and Burnett followed heavily. Lucretia was within; she had heard voices and had risen. As Caldwell entered she ran to him and clasped his arm. Burnett faced them.

"Well," said Caldwell, at last, breaking a momentous silence. "Here is the lady you wanted to see. Say what you have to say, please, and have done with it. We are particularly engaged to-night."

The outrageous nature of this last remark was apparently lost upon the navvy. He was looking at Lucretia intently. He had never ceased looking at her since he had entered the room. Lucretia looked only at her lover.

Suddenly Burnett ran forward with extended arms. "Oh, my lass!" he cried; "my dear, own lass! come home with me again, an' we'll forget all this! Come home with me, Lucy! come home, my poor dear! Oh, do come home!"

Two scalding tears slowly trickled down the navvy's weather-beaten cheeks. Lucretia shot a glance towards him. There was no relenting in her eyes.

"You see she won't come," began Caldwell, lightly, after another pause. "She doesn't want——"

"Let her speak herself," broke in Burnett, hoarsely. "You've
spoke

spoke too much for her, as well as to her, damn you ! Now don't interfere now between man and wife ! "

" Don't you coerce her," retorted Caldwell, blandly. " She knows her own mind, I should hope ! If she doesn't want to come back to you, she doesn't ! "

" Well, let her speak for herself, for God Almighty's sake," cried Burnett. " An' don't put your words into her mouth."

" Answer him, dear," said Caldwell, turning his face towards Lucretia. "And in your own words, as your heart dictates. Choose, Lucy ! will you have him or me ? "

" Oh ! Jamie, Jamie ! "

" You see," said Caldwell, holding Lucretia to his heart, as he faced the speechless man, a few paces in front of him. " She chooses me."

Burnett's mouth opened and shut. He said nothing.

" She made a mistake when she married you," said Caldwell, coolly. " She found it out when she saw me, and now she's rectifying it. It's quite natural, you know, and an event of every day occurrence."

" I don't know about no ev'ry day 'vents," sobbed the navvy. " But I know you've broke my heart, an' I hope you'll burn in hell fires ! "

Lucretia's flaming face looked up above Caldwell's caressing arms.

" And if he does," she cried back, " by God Almighty, John Burnett ! I'll burn with him too ! "

Her fierce, adoring eyes devoured her lover's face. Caldwell bent his head till his lips met hers.

Burnett heard their kiss as he went heavily out.

He crossed the threshold and drew the door sharply to behind him. Then he turned, swiftly, impulsively. Lucretia's

name

name choked in his throat. The hard, unyielding door reminded him of the futility of his effort, and he laughed, mocking, in his anguish, his own bitter mistake. There was no moon ; the twilight had passed, leaving the darker night behind. A tear stood out on his worn, whitened cheeks and his teeth clenched on a sob, when he lifted the latch of his house door and passed into his dishonoured home.

" The childern's gone, too," he said again, gazing round the empty room, in dreary, vacant misery. " But this aunt'll bring 'em back ag'in some day, when Molly's grown more handylike, to shift for me an' the little uns alone. An' I'll stay on 'ere till they comes. I'll not go too. An' p'raps—p'raps—she'll come back too, some day. . . ."

He stumbled, slowly and awkwardly, up and down his kitchen, painfully working out his scheme of the future in his dull, heavy brain. " I don't understand her," he muttered again, his future revolving round his wife as its sole, eternal pivot. He had not yet realised that Lucretia was lost to him for ever. " I don't understand her," he groaned, " nor any woman ; but p'raps she'll grow tired and 'ave no place to lay her tired 'ead in—my poor lass !—an' p'raps she'll remember our only home we ever 'ad together, she an' me, an' so p'raps she'll come back to it at last. If I goes on livin' 'ere, same as ever, p'raps she'll come back at last."

Dawn broke over the grey wilderness of slate roofs, over the railroad, where it circled round the eastern suburb of the town, over the dreary brickfields.

" I'll light a fire, so as she'll see there's no change 'ere," thought Burnett, setting, awkwardly enough, to his unwonted task. A fitful eagerness flashed over his stolid face.

There was a slight breeze from the west. The pale, twisted
smoke

smoke column from Burnett's chimney overtook the larger
volume that was gaily spouting from the big chimney on the
assistant superintendent's house. Both were mingled together as
they were blown, eastwards, over the town. At his usual time
Burnett went down to his work on the line.

"If so be as she gives a thought to—to what she's left be'ind,"
he thought, "she'll see me goin' an' think I'm the same as usual.
'Twill make 'er comin' back the easier."

He clung to the one remaining hope that Lucretia's faithlessness
had not uprooted and cast out of his life. Without that anchor
to his miserable soul he would have been like a ship adrift on an
open sea, and shipwreck would speedily have followed. Contrary
to habit, he went home at midday, to eat his dinner in his own
house.

"'Twill seem more—more homelike," he thought. "An'
'twill be another chanst for 'er to see I'm not meanin' to leave my
home."

The long, hot afternoon of toil dragged to a weary close on the
line.

Burnett sat by his cottage door, staring, steadily, across the
railroad. The sun went slowly down beyond the deserted
brickfields; the twilight drew closer around him, and shut him
in, alone. A board with "To Let" written across it, in bright
black letters, had been set up above the fence in front of the
assistant superintendent's late home, since midday.

"But she'll come back some day," thought Burnett. His dry,
miserable eyes looked, blankly, into the growing darkness. "She
must—she must do that! She must know—she looked at my
chimney as she . . . as she went . . . an' she must know how I
love her. . . ."

Night fell slowly over the town.

A Song

By John Davidson

London

A THWART the sky a lowly sigh
   From west to east the sweet wind carried ;
The sun stood still on Primrose Hill ;
  His light in all the city tarried :
The clouds on viewless columns bloomed
Like smouldering lilies unconsumed.

" Oh, sweetheart, see, how shadowy,
  Of some occult magician's rearing,
Or swung in space of Heaven's grace,
  Dissolving, dimly reappearing,
Afloat upon ethereal tides
St. Paul above the city rides ! "

A rumour broke through the thin smoke
  Enwreathing Abbey, Tower, and Palace,
The parks, the squares, the thoroughfares,
  The million-peopled lanes and alleys,
An ever-muttering prisoned storm,
The heart of London beating warm.

Two Pictures

By P. Wilson Steer

I. Portrait of Himself

II. The Mirror

The Haseltons

By Hubert Crackanthorpe

I

SHE sat in a corner of a large London drawing-room, and the two men stood before her—Hillier Haselton, her husband, and George Swann, her husband's cousin; and, beyond them, the mellow light of shaded candles, vague groupings of black coats, white shirt-fronts, and gay-tinted dresses, and the noisy hum of conversation.

The subject that the two men were discussing—and more especially Swann's blunt earnestness—stirred her, though throughout it she had been unpleasantly conscious of a smallness, almost a pettiness, in Hillier's aspect.

" Well, but why not, my dear Swann? Why not be unjust: man's been unjust to woman for so many years."

Hillier let his voice fall listlessly, as if to rebuke the other's vehemence; and to hint that he was tired of the topic, looked round at his wife, noting at the same time that Swann was observing how he held her gaze in his meaningly. And the unexpectedness of his own attitude charmed him—his hot defence of an absurd theory, obviously evoked by a lover-like desire to please her. Others, whose admiration he could trust, would, he surmised, have

reckoned

reckoned it a pretty pose.   And she, perceiving that Swann seemed to take her husband's sincerity for granted, felt a sting of quick regret that she had ever come to understand him, and that she could not still view him as they all viewed him.

Hillier moved away across the room, and Swann drew a stool beside her chair, and asking her for news of Claude, her little boy, talked to her of other things—quite simply, for they were grown like old friends.   He looked at her steadily, stroking his rough fair beard, as if he were anxious to convey to her something which he could not put into words.   She divined ; and, a little startled, tried to thank him with her eyes ; but, embarrassed by the clumsiness of his own attempt at sympathetic perception, he evidently noticed nothing.   And this obtuseness of his disappointed her, since it somehow seemed to confirm her isolation.

She glanced round the room.   Hillier stood on the hearth-rug, his elbow on the mantel-piece, busily talking, with slight deferential gestures, to the great English actress in whose honour the dinner had been given.   The light fell on his smooth glistening hair, on his quick sensitive face ; for the moment forcing herself to realise him as he appeared to the rest, she felt a thrill of jaded pride in him, in his cleverness, in his reputation, in his social success.

Swann, observing the direction of her gaze, said, almost apologetically, " You must be very proud of him."

She nodded, smiled a faint, assumed smile ; then added, adopting his tone, " His success has made him so happy."

" And you too ? " he queried.

" Of course," she answered quickly.

He stayed silent, while she continued to watch her husband absently.

Success,

II

Success, an atmosphere of flattery, suited Hillier Haselton, and stimulating his weaknesses, continually encouraged him to display the handsomer portion of his nature. For though he was yet young—and looked still younger—there was always apparent, beneath his frank boyish relish of praise, a semblance of serious modesty, a strain of genuine reserve. And society—the smart literary society that had taken him up—found this combination charming. So success had made life pleasant for him in many ways, and he rated its value accordingly; he was too able a man to find pleasure in the facile forms of conceit, or to accept, with more than a certain cynical complacency, the world's generous judgment on his work. Indeed, the whole chorus of admiration did but strengthen his contempt for contemporary literary judgments, a contempt which—lending the dignity of deliberate purpose to his indulgence of his own weakness for adulation—procured him a refined, a private, and an altogether agreeable self-satisfaction. When people set him down as vastly clever, he was pleased; he was unreasonably annoyed when they spoke of him as a great genius.

Life, he would repeat, was of larger moment than literature; and, despite all the freshness of his success, his interest in himself, in the play of his own personality, remained keener, and, in its essence, of more lasting a nature, than his ambition for genuine achievement. The world—people with whom he was brought into relation—stimulated him so far as he could assimilate them to his conception of his own attitude; most forms of art too, in great measure—and music altogether—attracted him in the pro-

portion

portion that they played upon his intimate emotions. Similarly, his friendships ; and for this reason he preferred the companionship of women. But since his egoism was uncommonly dexterous, he seemed endowed with a rare gift of artistic perception, of psychological insight, of personal charm.

It had always been his nature to live almost exclusively in the present ; his recollection of past impressions was grown scanty from habitual disuse. His sordid actions in the past he forgot with an ever-increasing facility ; his moments of generosity or self-sacrifice he remembered carelessly, and enjoyed a secret pride in their concealment ; and the conscious embellishment of subjective experience for the purpose of " copy," he had instinctively disdained.

Since his boyhood, religion had been distasteful to him, though, at rare moments, it had stirred his sensibilities strangely. Now, occasionally, the thought of the nullity of life, of its great unsatisfying quality, of the horrid squalor of death, would descend upon him with its crushing, paralysing weight ; and he would lament, with bitter, futile regret, his lack of a secure stand-point, and the continual limitations of his self-absorption ; but even that, perhaps, was a mere literary melancholy, assimilated from certain passages of Pierre Loti.

But now he had published a stout volume of critical essays, and an important volume of poetry, and society had clamorously ratified his own conception of himself. Certainly, now, in the eyes of the world, it was agreed beyond dispute that she, his wife, was of quite the lesser importance. " She was nice and quiet," which meant that she seemed mildly insignificant ; " she had a sense of humour," which meant that an odd note of half-stifled cynicism sometimes escaped her. He was evidently very devoted to her, and on that account women trusted him—all the more
because

because her personality possessed no obvious glamour. Perhaps, now and then, his attentions to her in public seemed a little ostentatious; but then, in these modern uncourtly days, that in itself was distinctive. In private too, especially at the moments when he found life stimulating, he was still tactful and expansive with sympathetic impulse; from habit; from pride in his comprehension of women; from dislike to cheap hypocrisy. How could he have divined that bitter suppressed seriousness, with which she had taken her disillusionment; when not once in three months did he consider her apart from the play of his own personality; otherwise than in the light of her initial attitude towards him?

And her disillusionment, how had it come? Certainly not with a rush of sudden overwhelming revelation; certainly it was in no wise inspired by the tragedy of Nora Helmer. It had been a gradual growth, to whose obscure and trivial beginnings she had not had the learning to ascribe their true significance. To sound the current of life was not her way. She was naïve by nature; and the ignorance of her girlhood had been due rather to a natural inobservance than to carefully managed surroundings. And yet, she had come to disbelieve in Hillier; to discredit his clever attractiveness: she had become acutely sensitive to his instability, and, with a secret, instinctive obstinacy, to mistrust the world's praise of his work. Perhaps, had he made less effort in the beginning to achieve a brilliancy of attitude in her eyes, had he schooled her to expect from him a lesser loftiness of aspiration, things might have been very different; or, at least, there might have resulted from the process of her disillusionment a lesser bitterness of conviction. But she had taken her marriage with so keen an earnestness of ideal, had noted every turn in his personality with so intense an expectation. Perhaps, too, had he

detected

detected the first totterings of her ideal conception of him, had he aided her, as it were, to descend his figure from that pedestal where he himself had originally planted it, together they might have set it uninjured on a lower and less exposed plane. But he had never heeded her subtle indications of its insecurity; alone, she had watched its peril, awaiting with a frightened fascination the day when it should roll headlong in the dust. And, at intervals, she would vaguely marvel, when she observed others whose superior perspicacity she assumed, display no perception of his insincerity. Then the oppressive sense that she—she, his wife, the mother of his child—was the only one who saw him clearly, and the unsurmountable shrinking from the relief of sharing this sense with any one, made her sourly sensitive to the pettiness, the meanness, the hidden tragic element in life.

A gulf had grown between—that was how she described it to herself. Outwardly their relations remained the same; but, frequently, in his continuance of his former attitude, she detected traces of deliberate effort; frequently when off his guard, he would abandon all pretension to it, and openly betray how little she had come to mean to him. There were, of course, moments also, when, at the echo of his tenderness, she would feverishly compel herself to believe in its genuineness; but a minute later he would have forgotten his exaltation, and, almost with irritation, would deliberately ignore the tense yearning that was glowing within her.

And so, the coming of his success—a brilliant blossoming into celebrity—had stirred her but fitfully. Critics wrote of the fine sincerity of his poetry; while she clung obstinately to her superstition that fine poetry must be the outcome of a great nobility of character. And, sometimes, she hated all this success of his, because it seemed to emphasise the gulf between them, and in some

some inexplicable way to lesson her value in his eyes : **then** again, from an impulse of sheer unselfishness, she would succeed in almost welcoming it, because, after all, he was her husband.

But of all this he noted nothing : only now and then he would remind himself vaguely that she had no literary leanings.

The little Claude was three years old. Before his birth, Hillier had dilated much on the mysterious beauty of childhood, had vied with her own awed expectation of the wonderful coming joy. During her confinement, which had been a severe one, for three nights in succession he had sat, haggard with sleepless anxiety, on a stiff-backed dining-room chair, till all danger was passed. But afterwards the baby had disappointed him sorely ; and later she thought he came near actively disliking it. Still, reminding herself of the winsomeness of other children at the first awakening of intelligence, she waited with patient hopefulness, fondly fancy-ing a beautiful boy-child ; wide baby eyes ; a delicious prattle. Claude, however, attained no prettiness, as he grew : from an unattractive baby he became an unattractive child, with lanky, carroty hair ; a squat nose ; an ugly, formless mouth. And in addition, he was fretful, mischievous, self-willed. Hillier at this time paid him but a perfunctory attention ; avoided discussing him ; and, when that was not possible, adopted a subtle, aggrieved tone that cut her to the quick. For she adored the child ; adored him because he was hers ; adored him for his very defects ; adored him because of her own suppressed sadness ; adored him for the prospect of the future—his education, his development, his gradual growth into manhood.

From the house in Cromwell Road the Haseltons had moved to a flat near Victoria Station : their means were moderate ; but now, through the death of a relative, Hillier was no longer dependent upon literature for a living.

George

III

George Swann was her husband's cousin; and besides, he had stood godfather to the little Claude. He was the elder by eight years; but Hillier always treated him as if their ages were reversed, and, before Ella, used to nickname him the "Anglo-Saxon," because of his loose physical largeness, his flaxen hair and beard, his strong simplicity of nature. And Swann, with a reticent good-humour, acquiesced in Hillier's tone towards him; out of vague regard for his cousin's ability; out of respect for him as Ella's husband.

Swann and Ella were near friends. Since their first meeting, the combination of his blunt self-possession and his uncouth timidity with women, had attracted her. Divining his simplicity, she had felt at once at her ease with him, and, treating him with open cousinly friendliness, had encouraged him to come often to the house.

A while later, a trivial incident confirmed her regard for him. They had been one evening to the theatre together—she and Hillier and Swann—and afterwards, since it was raining, she and Hillier waited under the door-way while he sallied out into the Strand to find them a cab. Pushing his way along the crowded street, his eyes scanning the traffic for an empty hansom, he accidentally collided with a woman of the pavement, jostling her off the kerb into the mud of the gutter. Ella watched him stop, gaze ruefully at the woman's splashed skirt, take off his hat, and apologise with profuse, impulsive regret. The woman continued her walk, and presently passed the theatre door. She looked middle aged : her face was hard and animal-like.

One

One Sunday afternoon—it was summer-time—as she was crossing the park to pay a call in Gloucester Square, she came across him sauntering alone in Kensington Gardens. She stopped and spoke to him : he seemed much startled to meet her. Three-quarters of an hour later, when she returned, he was sitting on a public bench beside her path ; and immediately, from his manner, she half-guessed that he had been waiting for her. It was a fortnight after Claude's christening : he started to speak to her of the child, and so, talking together gravely, they turned on to the turf, mounted the slope, and sat down on two chairs beneath the trees.

Touched by his waiting for her, she was anxious to make friends with him ; because he was the baby's godfather ; because he seemed alone in the world ; because she trusted in his goodness. So she led him, directly and indirectly, to talk of himself. At first, in moody embarrassment, he prodded the turf with his stick ; and presently responded, unwillingly breaking down his troubled reserve, and alluding to his loneliness confidingly, as if sure of her sympathy.

Unconsciously he made her feel privileged thus to obtain an insight into the inner workings of his heart, and gave her a womanly, sentimental interest in him.

Comely cloud-billows were overhead, and there was not a breath of breeze.

They paused in their talk, and he spoke to her of Kensington Gardens, lovingly, as of a spot which had signified much to him in the past—Kensington Gardens, massively decorous ; ceremoniously quiet ; pompous, courtly as a king's leisure park ; the slow, opulent contours of portly foliage, sober-green, immobile and indolent ; spacious groupings of tree-trunks ; a low ceiling of leaves ; broad shadows mottling the grass. The Long Water,

smooth

smooth and dark as a mirror; lining its banks, the rhododendrons swelling with colour, cream, purple, and carmine. The peacock's insolent scream; a silently skimming pigeon; the joyous twitterings of birds; the patient bleating of sheep. . . .

At last she rose to go. He accompanied her as far as the Albert Memorial, and when he had left her, she realised, with a thrill of contentment, that he and she had become friends.

IV

That had been the beginning of George Swann's great love for her. His was a slowly-moving nature : it was gradually therefore that he came to value, as a matter of almost sacred concern, the sense of her friendship; reverencing her with the single-hearted, unquestioning reverence of a man unfamiliar with women; regarding altogether gravely her relations with him—their talks on serious subjects, the little letters she wrote to him, the books that he had given to her—Swinburne's *Century of Roundels ;* a tiny edition of Shelley, bound in white parchment; Mrs. Meynell's *Rhythm of Life*. He took to studying her intellectual tastes, the topics that were congenial to her, her opinions on men and women, with a quiet, plodding earnestness; almost as if it were his duty. Thus he learned her love of simple country things; gained a conception of her girlhood's home; of her father and mother, staid country folk. He did not know how to him alone she could talk of these things; or of the warm, deep-seated gratitude she bore him in consequence; but he reverted constantly to the topic, because, under its influence, she always brightened, and it seemed to ratify the bond of sympathy between them.

How

How much, as the months went by, she came to mean to him, he had not in the least realised : he had never thought of her as playing a part in his own life ; only as a beautiful-natured woman, to whom he owed everything, because, by some strange chance, she had made him her friend.

Not even in his moments of idle vagrant reverie, did he think to ask more of her than this. To intrude himself further into her life, to offer her more than exactly that which she was expecting of him, naturally never occurred to him. Yet, in a queer uncomfortable way, he was jealous of other men's familiarity with her—vaguely jealous lest they should supplant him, mistrustful of his own modesty. And there was no service which, if she had asked it of him, he would not have accomplished for·her sake ; for he had no ties.

But towards Hillier, since he belonged to her, Swann's heart warmed affectionately : she had loved and married him ; had made him master of her life. So he instinctively extended to his cousin a portion of the unspoken devotion inspired by Ella. Such was the extent of his reverence for her, and his diffidence regarding himself, that he took for granted that Hillier was an ideal husband, tender, impelled by her to no ordinary daily devotion : for, that it should be otherwise, would have seemed to him a monstrous improbability. Yet latterly, since the coming of Hillier's success, certain incidents had disconcerted him, filled him with ill-defined uneasiness.

From the first, he had been one of Hillier's warmest admirers ; praising, whenever an opportunity offered, out of sheer loyalty to Ella, and pride in his cousin, the fineness of form that his poetry revealed. To her, when they were alone, he had talked in the same enthusiastic strain : the first time she had seemed listless and tired, and afterwards he had blamed himself for his want of

tact ;

tact ; on another occasion, he had brought her a laudatory article, and she had turned the conversation brusquely into another channel. And, since his love for her—of which as yet he was himself unconscious—caused him to brood over means of pleasing her (he lived alone in the Temple), this indication that he had jarred her sensibilities was not lost upon him.

Hillier's attitude towards the little Claude, and the pain that it was causing her, would in all probability have escaped him, had she not alluded to it once openly, frankly assuming that he had perceived it. It was not indeed that she was in any way tempted to indulge in the transitional treachery of discussing Hillier with him ; but that, distressed, yearning for counsel, she was prompted almost irresistibly to turn to Swann, who had stood godfather to the child, who was ready to join her in forming anxious speculations concerning the future.

For of course he had extended his devotion to the child also, who, at Hillier's suggestion, was taught to call him Uncle George. Naturally his heart went out to children : the little Claude, since the first awakening of his intelligence, had exhibited a freakish, childish liking for him ; and, in his presence, always assumed something of the winsomeness of other children.

The child's preference for Swann, his shy mistrust of his father, were sometimes awkwardly apparent ; but Hillier, so it seemed to Ella, so far from resenting, readily accepted his cousin's predominance. " Children always instinctively know a good man," he would say ; and Ella would wince inwardly, discerning, beneath his air of complacent humility, how far apart from her he had come to stand.

Thus, insensibly, Swann had become necessary to her, almost the pivot, as it were, of her life : to muse concerning the nature of his feelings towards her, to probe its sentimental aspects, to accept

his

his friendship otherwise than with unconscious ease, that was not her way.

But Hillier noted critically how things were drifting, and even lent encouragement to their progress in a way that was entirely unostentatious; since so cynical an attitude seemed in some measure to justify his own conduct.

V

For he was unfaithful to his wife. It was inevitable that the temptation, in the guise of a craving for change, should come—not from the outside, but from within himself. And he had no habit of stable purpose with which to withstand it. Not altogether was it a vagrant, generalised lusting after women other than his wife; not a mere harking back to the cruder experiences of his bachelorhood; though, at first it had seemed so to manifest itself. Rather was it the result of a moody restlessness, of a dissatisfaction (with her, consciously, no; for the more that he sinned against her, the more lovable, precious her figure appeared to him) kindled by continual contact with natural goodness. It was as if, in his effort to match his personality with hers, he had put too severe a strain upon the better part of him.

He himself had never analysed the matter more exhaustively than this. The treacherous longing had gripped him at certain moments, holding him helpless as in a vice. He had conceived no reckless passion for another woman: such an eventuality, he dimly surmised, was well-nigh impossible. In his case brain domineered over heart; to meet the first outbursting of his adoration for his wife, he had drained every resource of his sentimentality.

Was it then an idle craving for adventure, a school-boy curiosity
clamouring

clamouring for fresh insight into the heart of women? Mere experience was unnecessary for the attainment of comprehension : " to have lived " did not imply " to have understood " : the most pregnant adventures, as he knew, were those which entailed no actual unfaithfulness.

And for these—subtle, psychological intimacies—ample occasion offered. Yet the twist in his nature led him to profess to treat them heedlessly ; and, in reality, to prosecute them with no genuine strenuousness. They would have been obvious lapses ; Ella would have been pained, pitied perhaps : from that his vanity and his sham chivalry alike shrank.

His unfaithfulness to her, then, had been prompted by no evident motive. Superficially considered, it seemed altogether gratuitous, meaningless. The world—that is, people who knew him and her —would probably have discredited the story, had it come to be bruited. And this fact he had not omitted to consider.

She, the other woman, was of little importance. She belonged to the higher walks of the demi-monde : she was young ; beautiful, too, in a manner ; light-hearted ; altogether complaisant. She was not the first : there had been others before her ; but these were of no account whatsoever : they had but represented the bald fact of his unfaithfulness. But *she* attracted him : he returned to her again and again ; though afterwards, at any rate in the beginning, he was wont to spare himself little in the matter of self-reproach, and even to make some show of resisting the temptation. The discretion of her cynical camaraderie, however, was to be trusted ; and that was sufficient to undermine all virtuous resolution. She had the knack, too, of cheering him when depressed, and, curiously enough, of momentarily reinstating him in his own conceit, though later, on his return to Ella, he would suffer most of the pangs of remorse.

There

There was something mannish about her—not about her physiognomy, but about her mind—derived, no doubt, from the scantiness of her intercourse with women. Her cynicism was both human and humorous : she was a person of little education, and betrayed none of the conventionality of her class : hence her point of view often struck him as oddly direct and unexpected. He used to talk to her about himself, candidly discussing all manner of random and intimate matters before her, without shyness on his part, without surprise on hers—almost at times as if she were not present—and with an assumption of facile banter, to listen to which tickled his vanity. Only to Ella did he never allude ; and in this, of course, she tacitly acquiesced. She possessed a certain quality of sympathetic tact ; always attentive to his talk, never critical of it ; mindful of all that he had previously recounted. He could always resume his attitude at the very point where he had abandoned it. Between them there was never any aping of sentimentality.

That she comprehended him—with so fatuous a delusion he never coquetted : nor that she interested him as a curious type. She saw no subtle significance in his talk : she understood nothing of its complex promptings : she was ordinary, uneducated, and yet stimulating—and that was the contrast which attracted him towards her. Concerning the course of her own existence he did not trouble himself : he accepted her as he found her ; deriving a sense of security from the fact that towards him her manner varied but little from visit to visit. But, as these accumulated, becoming more and more regular, and his faith in her discretion blunted the edge of his remorse, he came to notice how she braced him, reconciled him to his treachery (which, he argued, in any case was inevitable) ; lent to it a spice almost of pleasantness. Neither had he misgivings of the future, of how it would end.

end.   One day she would pass out of his life as easily as she had
come into it.   His relations with her were odd, though not in the
obvious way.   About the whole thing he was insensibly coming
to feel composed.

And its smoothness, its lack of a disquieting aspect, impelled
him to persevere towards Ella in cheerfulness, courteous kindness,
and a show of continuous affection ; and to repent altogether of
those lapses into roughness which had marred the first months of
their marriage.

VI

The hansoms whirled their yellow, gleaming eyes down West :
hot, flapping gusts went and returned aimlessly ; and the mirthless
twitterings of the women fell abruptly on the sluggishly shuffling
crowd.   All the sin of the city seemed crushed to listlessness ;
vacantly wistful, the figures waited by the street corners.

Then the storm burst.   Slow, ponderous drops : a clap of the
thunder's wrath ; a crinkled rim of light, unveiling a slab of sky,
throbbing, sullen and violet ; small, giggling screams of alarm,
and a stampede of bunchy silhouettes.   The thunder clapped
again, impatient and imperious ; and the rain responded, zealously
hissing.   Bright stains of liquid gold straggled across the roadway ; a sound of splashing accompanied the thud of hoofs, the
rumble of wheels, the clanking of chains, and the ceaseless rattle
of the drops on the hurried procession of umbrellas.

Swann, from the corner of a crowded omnibus, peered absently
through the doorway, while the conductor, leaning into the street,
touted mechanically for passengers.

The vehicle stopped.   A woman, bare-headed and cloaked,
escorted by the umbrella of a restaurant official, hurried to the
                                                              shelter

shelter of a cab, across the wet pavement. A man broke the stream of the hastening crowd; halted beside the wheel to stare. The woman laughed in recognition, noisily. The man stepped rapidly on to the foot-board, and an instant stood there, directing the driver across the roof. The light from a lamp-post caught his face: it was Hillier. The next moment he was seated beside the woman, who was still laughing (Swann could see the gleaming whiteness of her teeth): the driver had loosened the window strap, the glass had slid down, shutting them in. The omnibus jolted forward, and the cab followed in its wake, impatiently, for the street was blocked with traffic.

Immediately, with a fierce vividness, Ella's image sprang up before Swann's eyes—her face with all its pure, natural, simple sweetness. And there—not ten yards distant, behind the obscurity of that blurred glass, Hillier was sitting with another woman—a woman concerning whose status he could not doubt.

He clenched his gloved fists. The wild impulse spurted forth, the impulse to drag the cur from the cab, to bespatter him, to throw him into the mud, to handle him brutally, as he deserved. It was as if Hillier had struck him a cowardly blow in the face.

Then the hansom started to creep past the omnibus. Swann sprang into the roadway. A moment later he was inside another cab, whirling in pursuit down Piccadilly hill.

The horse's hoofs splashed with a rhythmical, accelerated precision: he noticed dully how the crupper-strap flapped from side to side, across the animal's back. Ahead, up the incline, pairs of tiny specks, red and green, were flitting.

" It's the cab with the lady what come out of the restaurant, ain't it, sir ? "

" Yes," Swann called back through the trap.

The reins tightened: the horse quickened his trot.

Hyde

Hyde Park Corner stood empty and resplendent with a glitter of glamorous gold. The cab turned the corner of Hamilton Place, and the driver lashed the house into a canter up Park Lane.

" That's 'im—jest in front——"

" All right. Follow." Swann heard himself answering. And, amid his pain, he was conscious that's the man's jaunty tone seemed to indicate that this sort of job was not unfamiliar.

He struggled to tame the savageness of his indignation ; to think out the situation ; to realise things coolly, that he might do what was best for her. But the leaping recollection of all her trustfulness, her goodness, filled him with a burning, maddening compassion. . . . He could see nothing but the great wrong done to her. . . .

Where were they going—the green lights of that cab in front—that woman and Hillier ? . . . Where would it end, horrible pursuit—this whirling current which was sweeping him forward. . . . It was like a nightmare. . . .

He must stop them—prevent this thing . . . but, evidently, this was not the first time. . . . Hillier and this woman knew one another. He had stopped, on catching sight of her, and she had recognised him. . . . The thing might have been going on for weeks—for months. . . .

. . . Yet he must stop them—not here, in the crowded street (they were in the Edgware Road), but later, when they had reached their destination—where there were no passers—where it could be done without scandal. . . .

. . . Yes, he must send Hillier back to her. . . . And she believed in him—trusted him. . . . She must know nothing—at all costs, he must spare her the hideous knowledge—the pain of it. . . . And yet—and yet ? . . . Hillier—the blackguard—she would
have

have to go on living with him, trusting him, confiding in him, loving him. . . .

And for relief he returned wearily to his indignation.

How was it possible for any man—married to her—to be so vile, so false ? . . . The consummate hypocrisy of it all. . . .

Swann remembered moments when Hillier's manner towards her had appeared redolent of deference, of suppressed affection. And he—a man of refinement—not a mere coarse-fibred, sensual brute—he who wrote poetry—Swann recalled a couplet full of fine aspiration—that he should have done this loathsome thing—done it callously, openly—any one might have seen it—deceived her for some common vulgar, public creature. . . .

Suddenly the cab halted abruptly.

" They're pulled up, across the street there," the driver whispered hoarsely, confidentially ; and for his tone Swann could have struck him.

It was an ill-lit street, silent and empty. The houses were low, semi-detached, and separated from the pavement by railings and small gardens.

The woman had got out of the cab and was pushing open the swing-gate. Hillier stood on the foot-board, paying the cabman. Swann, on the opposite side of the street, hesitated. Hillier stepped to the pavement, and ran lightly up the door-steps after the woman. She unlocked the door : it closed behind them. And the hansom which had brought them turned, and trotted away down the street.

Swann stood a moment before the house, irresolute. Then re-crossed the street slowly. And a hansom, bearing a second couple, drew up at the house next door.

" You

VII

" You can go to bed, Hodgson.   I will turn off the light."

The man retired silently. It was a stage-phrase that rose unconsciously to her lips, a stage-situation with which she was momentarily toying.

Alone, she perceived its absurd unreality.   Nothing, of course, would happen to-night : though so many days and nights she had been waiting.   The details of life were clumsy, cumbersome : the simplification of the stage, of novels, of dozing dreams, seemed, by contrast, bitterly impossible.

She took up the book again, and read on, losing herself for a while in the passion of its pages—a passion what was all glamorous, sentimental felicity, at once vague and penetrating.   But, as she paused to reach a paper-knife, she remembered the irrevocable, prosaic groove of existence, and that slow drifting to a dreary commonplace—a commonplace that was *hers*—brought back all her aching listlessness.   She let the book slip to the carpet.

Love, she repeated to herself, a silken web, opal-tinted, veiling all life ; love, bringing fragrance and radiance ; love with the moonlight streaming across the meadows ; love, amid summer-leafed woods, a sparkle in the morning sun ; a simple clasping of hands ; a happiness, child-like and thoughtless, secure and intimate. . . .

And she—she had nothing—only the helpless child ; her soul was brave and dismantled and dismal ; and once again started the gnawing of humiliation—inferior even to the common people, who could be loved and forget, in the midst of promiscuous squalor.   Without love, there seemed no reason for life.

Away

Away her thoughts sailed to the tale of the fairy-prince, stepping to shore in his silver armour, come to deliver and to love. She would have been his in all humility, waited on him in fearful submission; she would have asked for nought but his love.

Years ago, once or twice, men had appeared to her like that. And Hillier, before they were married, when they were first engaged. A strange girl she must have been in those days! And now—now they were like any husband and any wife.

"It happened by chance," the old tale began. Chance! Yes, it was chance that governed all life; mocking, ironical chance, daintily sportive chance, hobbled to the clumsy mechanism of daily existence.

Twelve o'clock struck. Ten minutes more perhaps, and Hillier would be home. She could hear his tread; she could see him enter, take off his coat and gloves gracefully, then lift her face lightly in his two hands, and kiss her on the forehead. He would ask for an account of her day's doings; but he would never heed her manner of answering, for he would have begun to talk of himself. And altogether complacently would he take up the well-worn threads of their common life.

And she would go on waiting, and trifling with hopelessness, for in real life such things were impossible. Men were dull and incomplete, and could not understand a woman's heart. . . .

And so she would wait till he came in, and when he had played his part, just as she had imagined he would play it, she would follow him, in dumb docility, up-stairs to bed.

*   *   *   *   *

It was past one o'clock when he appeared. She had fallen asleep in the big arm-chair: her book lay in a heap on the carpet beside her. He crossed the room, but she did not awake.

One

One hand hung over the arm of the chair, limp and white and fragile; her head, bent over her breast, was coyly resting in the curve of her elbow; her hair was a little dishevelled; her breathing was soft and regular, like a child's.

He sat down noiselessly, awed by this vision of her. The cat, which had lain stretched on the hearth-rug, sprang into his lap, purring and caressing. He thought it strange that animals had no sense of human sinfulness, and recalled the devotion of the dog of a prostitute, whom he had known years and years ago. . . .

He watched her, and her unconsciousness loosed within him the sickening pangs of remorse. . . . He mused vaguely on suicide as the only fitting termination. . . . And he descended to cheap anathemas upon life. . . .

*   *   *   *   *

By-and-by she awoke, opening her eyes slowly, wonderingly. He was kneeling before her, kissing her hand with reverential precaution.

She saw tears in his eyes: she was still scarcely awake: she made no effort to comprehend; only was impulsively grateful, and slipping her arms behind his head, drew him towards her and kissed him on the eyes. He submitted, and a tear moistened her lips.

Then they went up-stairs.

And she, passionately clutching at every memory of their love, feverishly cheated herself into bitter self-upbraiding, into attributing to him a nobility of nature that set him above all other men. And he, at each renewed outburst of her wild straining towards her ideal, suffered, as if she had cut his bare flesh with a whip.

It was his insistent attitude of resentful humility that finally wearied her of the fit of false exaltation. When she sank to sleep, the old ache was at her heart.

Swann

VIII

Swann strode into the room. Hillier looked up at him from his writing-table in unfeigned surprise; greeted him cordially, with a couple of trite, cheery remarks concerning the weather, then waited abruptly for an explanation of this morning visit; for Swann's trouble was written on his face.

"You look worried. Is there anything wrong?" Hillier asked presently.

"Yes."

"Well, can I do anything? If I can be of any service to you, old fellow, you know I——"

"I discovered last night what a damned blackguard you are." He spoke savagely, as if his bluntness exulted him: his tone quivered with suppressed passion.

Hillier, with a quick movement of his head, flinched as if he had been struck in the face. And the lines about his mouth were set rigidly.

There was a long, tense silence. Hillier was drawing circles on a corner of the blotting-pad; Swann was standing over him, glaring at him with a fierce, hateful curiosity. Hillier became conscious of the other's expression, and his fist clenched obviously.

"I saw you get into a cab with that woman," Swann went on. "I was in an omnibus going home. I followed you—drove after you. I wanted to stop you—to stop it—I was too late."

"Ah!" An exasperated, sneering note underlined the exclamation. Hillier drove the pen-point into the table. The nib curled and snapped.

The

The blood rushed to Swann's forehead. In a flash he caught a glimpse of the thought that had crossed Hillier's mind. It was like a personal indignity; he struggled desperately to control himself.

Hillier looked straight into his cousin's distorted face. At the sight the tightness about his own mouth slackened. His composure returned.

" I'm sorry. Forgive me," he said simply.

" How can you be such a brute ? " Swann burst out unheeding. " Don't you care ? Is it nothing to you to wreck your wife's whole happiness—to spoil her life, to break her heart, to deceive her in the foulest way, to lie to her. Haven't you any conscience, any chivalry ? "

The manly anguish in his voice was not lost upon Hillier. He thought he realised clearly how it was for Ella, and not for him, that Swann was so concerned. Once more he took stock of his cousin's agitation, and a quick glitter came into his eyes. He felt as if a mysterious force had been suddenly given to him. Still he said nothing.

" How could you, Hillier ? How came you to do it ? "

" Sit down." He spoke coldly, clearly, as if he were playing a part which he knew well.

Swann obeyed mechanically.

" It's perfectly natural that you should speak to me like that. You take the view of the world. The view of the world I accept absolutely. Certainly I am utterly unworthy of Ella " (he mentioned her name with a curious intonation of assertive pride). " How I have sunk to this thing—the whole story of how I have come to risk my whole happiness for the sake of another woman, who is nothing—absolutely nothing—to me, to whom I am nothing, I won't attempt to explain. Did I attempt to do so,

I see

I see little probability of your understanding it, and little to be gained even if you did so. I choose to let it remain for you a piece of incomprehensible infamy : I have no wish to alter your view of me."

" You don't care . . . you've no remorse . . . you're callous and cynical. . . . Good God ! it's awful."

" Yes, Swann, I care," Hillier resumed, lowering his voice, and speaking with a slow distinctness, as if he were putting an excessive restraint upon his emotions. " I care more than you or any one will ever know."

" It's horrible. . . . I don't know what to think. . . . Don't you see the awfulness of your wife's position ? . . . Don't you realise the hideousness of what you've done ? "

" My dear Swann, nobody is more alive to the consequences of what I've done than I am. I have behaved infamously—I don't need to be told that by you. And whatever comes to me out of this thing " (he spoke with a grave, resigned sadness) " I shall bear it."

" Good God ! Can you think of nothing but yourself ? Can't you see that you've been a miserable, selfish beast—that what happens to you matters nothing ? Can't you see that the only thing that matters is your wife ? You're a miserable, skulking cur—— . . . She trusted you—she believed in you, and you've done her an almost irreparable wrong."

Hillier stood suddenly erect.

" What I have done, Swann, is more than a wrong. It is a crime. Within an hour of your leaving this room, I shall have told Ella everything. That is the only thing left for me to do, and I shall not shirk it. I shall take the full responsibility. You did right to come to me as you did. You are right to consider me a miserable, skulking cur " (he brought the words

out

out with an emphasised bravery). "Now you can do no more. The remainder of the matter rests between me and my wife——"

He paused.

"And to think that you——" Swann began passionately.

"There is no object to be gained by our discussing the matter further," Hillier interrupted a little loudly, but with a concentrated calm. "There is no need for you to remain here longer." He put his thumb to the electric bell.

"The maid will be here in a moment to show you out," he added.

Swann waited, blinking with hesitation. His personality seemed to be slipping from him.

"You are going to tell her?" he repeated slowly.

The door opened: he hurried out of the room.

The outer door slammed: Hillier's face turned a sickly white; his eyes dilated, and he laughed excitedly—a low, short, hysterical laugh. He looked at the clock: the whole scene had lasted but ten minutes. He pulled a chair to the fire, and sat staring at the flames moodily. . . . The tension of the dramatic situation snapped. Before his new prospect, once again he thought weakly of suicide. . . .

IX

He had told her—not, of course, the whole story—from that his sensitivity had shrunk. Still he had besmirched himself bravely; he had gone through with the interview not without dignity. Beforehand he had nerved himself for a terrible ordeal; yet, somehow, as he reviewed it, now that it was all over, the scene seemed to have fallen flat. The tragedy of her grief, of his

own

own passionate repentance, which he had been expecting, had proved unaccountably tame. She cried, and at the sight of those tears of hers he had suffered intensely; but she had displayed no suppressed, womanish jealousy; had not, in her despair, appeared to regard his confession as an overwhelming shattering of her faith in him, and so provoked him to reveal the depth of his anguish. He had implored her forgiveness; he had vowed he would efface the memory of his treachery; she had acquiesced dreamily, with apparent heroism. There had been no mention of a separation.

And now the whole thing was ended: to-night he and she were dining out.

He was vaguely uncomfortable; yet his heart was full of a sincere repentance, because of the loosening of the strain of his anxiety; because of the smarting sense of humiliation, when he recollected Swann's words; because he had caused her to suffer in a queer, inarticulate way, which he did not altogether understand, of which he was vaguely afraid. . . .

X

When at last he had left her alone, it was with a curious calmness that she started to reflect upon it all. She supposed it was very strange that his confession had not wholly prostrated her; and glancing furtively backwards, catching a glimpse of her old girlish self, wondered listlessly how it was that, insensibly, all these months, she had grown so hardened. . . .

*   *   *   *   *

By-and-by, the recent revelation of his unfaithfulness seemed to recede slowly into the misty past, and, fading, losing its sharp-

ness

ness of outline, its distinctness of detail, to resemble an irreparab
fact to which familiarity had inured her.

And all the uneasiness of her mistrustfulness, and pain of h
fluctuating doubtings ceased; her comprehension of him was a
at once clarified, rendered vivid and indisputable; and she w
conscious of a certain sense of relief. She was eased of tho
feverish, spasmodic gaspings of her half-starved love; at first tl
dulness of sentimental atrophy seemed the more endurable. Sl
jibed at her own natural artlessness; and insisted to herself th
she wanted no fool's paradise, that she was even glad to see him
he really was, to terminate, once for all, this futile folly of lov
that, after all, his unfaithfulness was no unusual and terrib
tragedy, but merely a commonplace chapter in the lives of smilin
chattering women, whom she met at dinners, evening parti
and balls. . . .

*   *   *   *   *

There were some who simpered to her over Hillier as
model of modern husbands; and she must go on listening ar
smiling. . . .

. . . And the long years ahead would unroll themselves—a slo
tale of decorous lovelessness. . . .

He would be always the same—that was the hardest to fac
His nature could never alter, grow into something different . .
never, never change . . . always, always the same. . . .

Oh! it made her dread it all—the restless round of social enjo
ments; the greedy exposure of the petty weaknesses of comm
acquaintance; the ill-natured atmosphere that she felt emanatir
from people herded together. . . . All the details of her Lordo
life looked unreal, mean, pitiful. . . .

And she longed after the old days of her girlhood, of the smoot
staid country life; she longed after the simple, restful companio
sh

hip of her old father and mother; after the accumulation of little
ncidents that she had loved long ago. . . . She longed too—and
he straining at heart-strings grew tenser—she longed after her own
ost maidenhood; she longed to be ignorant and careless; to see
fe once again as a simple, easy matter; to know nothing of evil;
o understand nothing of men; to trust—to trust unquestioningly.
. . All that was gone; she herself was all changed; those days
ould never come again. . . .

And she cried to herself a little, from weakness of spirit,
oftly. . . .

* * * * *

Then, gradually, out of the weary turmoil of her bitterness,
here came to her a warm impulse of vague sympathy for the
ountless, unknown tragedies at work around her; she thought of
he sufferings of outcast women—of loveless lives, full of mirth-
ess laughter; she thought of the long loneliness of childless
omen. . . .

She clutched for consolation at the unhappiness of others; but
he only discovered the greater ugliness of the world. And she
eturned to a tired contemplation of her own prospect. . . .

* * * * *

He had broken his vows to her—not only the solemn vow he
ad taken in the church (she recalled how his voice had trembled
vith emotion as he had repeated the words)—but all that passion-
te series of vows he had made to her during the spring-time of
heir love. . . .

. . . Yes, that seemed the worst part of it—that, and not the
naking love to another woman. . . . What was she like? . . .
Vhat was it in her that had attracted him? . . . Oh! but what
id that matter? . . . —only why were men's natures so different
:om women's? . . .

Now,

. . . Now, she must go on—go on alone.   Since her marriage sh
had lost the habit of daily converse with Christ : here in Londo
somehow, He had seemed so distant, so difficult of approach. . .

. . . She must just go on. . . . She had the little Claude. . .
It was to help her that God had given her Claude. . . . Oh ! sh
would pray to God to make him good—to give him a straigh
strong, upright, honest nature.   And herself, every day, she woul
watch over his growth, guide him, teach him. . . . Yes, he *mu*
grow up good . . . into boyhood . . . different from other bo
. . . into manhood, simple, honourable manhood. . . . She wou
be everything to him : he and she would come to comprehend eac
other, to read into each other's hearts. . . . Perhaps, betwee
them, would spring up perfect love and trust. . . .

XI

Swann had written to her :
" You are in trouble : let me come."

Gradually, between the lines of the note, she understood it a
—she read how his love for her had leapt up, now that he kne
that she was unhappy ; how he wanted to be near her, to comfo
her, and perhaps . . . perhaps . . .

She was filled with great sorrow for him—and warm gratitud
too, for his simple, single-hearted love—but sorrow, that she cou
give him nothing in return, and because it seemed that, som
how, he and she were about to bid·one another good-bye ; sh
thought she dimly foresaw how their friendship was doomed
dwindle. . . .

So she let him come.

*   *   *   *   *

Ar

. . . And all this she fancied she read again in the long, grave glance of his greeting, and the firm clasp of his big hand.

When he spoke, his deep, steady voice dominated her : she knew at once that he would do what was right.

" Ella, my poor Ella, how brave you are ! " She looked up at him, smiling tremulously, through her quick-starting tears. . . . The next moment it was as if the words had escaped him—almost as if he regretted them.

He sat down opposite her, and, lightening his voice, asked—just as he always did—for news of the little Claude.

And so their talk ran on.

After awhile, she came to realise that he meant to say no more : the strength of his great reserve became apparent, and a sense of peace stole over her. He talked on, and to the restful sound of his clear, strong voice, she abandoned herself dreamily. . . . This he had judged the better course. . . . that he should have adopted any other now seemed inconceivable. Beside him she felt weak and helpless : she remembered the loneliness of his life : he seemed to her altogether noble ; and she was vaguely remorseful that she had not perceived from the first that it was from him that her help would come. . . .

She divined, too, the fineness of his sacrifice—that manly, human struggle with himself, through which he had passed to attain it—how he had longed for the right to make her his . . . and how he had renounced. The sureness of his victory, and the hidden depths of his nature which it revealed awed her . . . now he would never swerve from what he knew to be right. . . . And on, through those years to come, she could trust him, always, always. . . .

. . . At last he bade her good-bye : even at the last his tone remained unchanged.

It

It was close upon seven o'clock. She went upstairs to dress for dinner, and kneeling beside the bed, prayed to God with an outburst of passionate, pulsing joy. . . .

Ten minutes later Hillier came in from his dressing-room. He clasped his hands round her bare neck, kissing her hair again and again.

" I have been punished, Nellie," he began in a broken whisper. " Good God ! it is hard to bear. . . . Help me, Nellie, . . . help me to bear it."

She unclasped his fingers, and started to stroke them ; a little mechanically, as if it were her duty to ease him of his pain. . . .

Passion

By Richard Garnett, LL.D., C.B.

THIS flame of Passion that so high in air,
    By spice and balsam of the spirit fed,
    With fire and fume vast Heaven hath overspread,
And blots the stars with smoke, or dims with glare :
Soon shall it droop, and radiance pure and fair
    Again from azure altitudes be shed ;
    And we the murky grime and embers red
Shall sift, if haply dust of Love be there.
Gather his ashes from the torrid mould,
    And, quenched with drops of Bacchic revelry,
    Yield to the Stygian powers to have and hold :
And urn Etrurian let his coffin be ;
    For this was made to store the dead and cold,
    And is a thing of much fragility.

The Reflected Faun

By Laurence Housman

Apple Blossom in Brittany

By Ernest Dowson

I

IT was the feast of the Assumption in Ploumariel, at the hottest part of the afternoon. Benedict Campion, who had just assisted at vespers, in the little dove-cotted church—like everything else in Ploumariel, even vespers were said earlier than is the usage in towns—took up his station in the market-place to watch the procession pass by. The head of it was just then emerging into the Square: a long file of men from the neighbouring villages, bare-headed and chaunting, followed the crucifer. They were all clad in the picturesque garb of the Morbihan peasantry, and were many of them imposing, quite noble figures with their clear-cut Breton features, and their austere type of face. After them a troop of young girls, with white veils over their heads, carrying banners—children from the convent school of the Ursulines ; and then, two and two in motley assemblage (peasant women with their white coifs walking with the wives and daughters of prosperous *bourgeois* in costumes more civilised but far less pictorial) half the inhabitants of Ploumariel—all, indeed, who had not, with Campion, preferred to be spectators, taking refuge from a broiling sun under the grateful shadow of the chest-

nuts

nuts in the market-place. Last of all a muster of clergy, four or
five strong, a small choir of bullet-headed boys, and the Curé or
the parish himself, Monsieur Letêtre chaunting from his book,
who brought up the rear.

Campion, leaning against his chestnut tree, watched them
defile. Once a smile of recognition flashed across his face, which
was answered by a girl in the procession. She just glanced from
her book, and the smile with which she let her eyes rest upon him
for a moment, before she dropped them, did not seem to detract
from her devotional air. She was very young and slight—she
might have been sixteen—and she had a singularly pretty face ;
her white dress was very simple, and her little straw hat, but both
of these she wore with an air which at once set her apart from her
companions, with their provincial finery and their rather commonplace charms. Campion's eyes followed the little figure until it
was lost in the distance, disappearing with the procession down a
by-street on its return journey to the church. And after they
had all passed, the singing, the last verse of the " Ave Maris
Stella," was borne across to him, through the still air, the voices of
children pleasantly predominating. He put on his hat at last, and
moved away ; every now and then he exchanged a greeting with
somebody—the communal doctor, the mayor ; while here and there
a woman explained him to her gossip in whispers as he passed, " It
is the Englishman of Mademoiselle Marie-Ursule—it is M. le
Curé's guest." It was to the dwelling of M. le Curé, indeed,
that Campion now made his way. Five minutes' walk brought
him to it ; an unpretentious white house, lying back in its large
garden, away from the dusty road. It was an untidy garden,
rather useful than ornamental ; a very little shade was offered by
one incongruous plane-tree, under which a wooden table was placed
and some chairs. After *déjeûner*, on those hot August days,
Campion

Campion and the Curé took their coffee here ; and in the evening
it was here that they sat and talked while Mademoiselle Hortense,
the Curé's sister, knitted, or appeared to knit, an interminable
shawl ; the young girl, Marie-Ursule, placidly completing the
quartet with her silent, felicitous smile of a convent-bred child,
which seemed sometimes, at least to Campion, to be after all a
finer mode of conversation.   He threw himself down now on the
bench, wondering when his hosts would have finished their de-
votions, and drew a book from his pocket as if he would read.
But he did not open it, but sat for a long time holding it idly in
his hand, and gazing out at the village, at the expanse of dark pine-
covered hills, and at the one trenchant object in the foreground,
the white façade of the convent of the Ursuline nuns.   Once and
again he smiled, as though his thoughts, which had wandered a
long way, had fallen upon extraordinarily pleasant things.   He was
a man of barely forty, though he looked slightly older than his
age : his little, peaked beard was grizzled, and a life spent in
literature, and very studiously, had given him the scholar's
premature stoop.   He was not handsome, but, when he smiled,
his smile was so pleasant that people credited him with good looks.
It brought, moreover, such a light of youth into his eyes, as to
suggest that if his avocations had unjustly aged his body, that had
not been without its compensations—his soul had remained remarkably young.   Altogether, he looked shrewd, kindly and
successful, and he was all these things, while if there was also a
certain sadness in his eyes—lines of lassitude about his mouth—
this was an idiosyncracy of his temperament, and hardly justified
by his history, which had always been honourable and smooth.
He was sitting in the same calm and presumably agreeable reverie,
when the garden gate opened, and a girl—the young girl of the
procession, fluttered towards him.

" Are

"Are you quite alone ? " she asked brightly, seating herself at his side. " Has not Aunt Hortense come back ? "

Campion shook his head, and she continued speaking in English, very correctly, but with a slight accent, which gave to her pretty young voice the last charm.

" I suppose she has gone to see *la mère Guémené.* She will not live another night they say. Ah ! what a pity," she cried, clasping her hands ; "to die on the Assumption—that is hard."

Campion smiled softly. " Dear child, when one's time comes, when one is old as that, the day does not matter much." Then he went on : " But how is it you are back ; were you not going to your nuns ? "

She hesitated a moment. " It is your last day, and I wanted to make tea for you. You have had no tea this year. Do you think I have forgotten how to make it, while you have been away, as I forget my English words ? "

" It's I who am forgetting such an English habit," he protested. " But run away and make it, if you like. I am sure it will be very good."

She stood for a moment looking down at him, her fingers smoothing a little bunch of palest blue ribbons on her white dress. In spite of her youth, her brightness, the expression of her face in repose was serious and thoughtful, full of unconscious wistfulness. This, together with her placid manner, the manner of a child who has lived chiefly with old people and quiet nuns, made her beauty to Campion a peculiarly touching thing. Just then her eyes fell upon Campion's wide-awake, lying on the seat at his side, and travelled to his uncovered head. She uttered a protesting cry : " Are you not afraid of a *coup de soleil?* See—you are not fit to be a guardian if you can be so foolish as that. It is I who have to look after you." She took up the great grey hat and set

set it daintily on his head ; then with a little laugh she disappeared into the house.

When Campion raised his head again, his eyes were smiling, and in the light of a sudden flush which just died out of it, his face looked almost young.

II

This girl, so foreign in her education and traditions, so foreign in the grace of her movements, in everything except the shade of her dark blue eyes, was the child of an English father ; and she was Benedict Campion's ward. This relation, which many persons found incongruous, had befallen naturally enough. Her father had been Campion's oldest and most familiar friend ; and when Richard Heath's romantic marriage had isolated him from so many others, from his family and from his native land, Campion's attachment to him had, if possible, only been increased. From his heart he had approved, had prophesied nothing but good of an alliance, which certainly, while it lasted, had been an wholly ideal relation. There had seemed no cloud on the horizon—and yet less than two years had seen the end of it. The birth of the child, Marie-Ursule, had been her mother's death ; and six months later, Richard Heath, dying less from any defined malady than because he lacked any longer the necessary motive to live, was laid by the side of his wife. The helpless child remained, in the guardianship of Hortense, her mother's sister, and elder by some ten years, who had already composed herself contentedly, as some women do, to the prospect of perpetual spinsterhood, and the care of her brother's house—an ecclesiastic just appointed curé of Ploumariel. And here, ever since, in this quiet corner of Brittany,

in

in the tranquil custody of the priest and his sister, Marie-Ursule
had grown up.

Campion's share in her guardianship had not been onerous,
although it was necessarily maintained ; for the child had inherited,
and what small property would come to her was in England, and
in English funds. To Hortense Letêtre and her brother such
responsibilities in an alien land were not for a moment to be
entertained. And gradually, this connection, at first formal and
impersonal, between Campion and the Breton presbytery, had
developed into an intimacy, into a friendship singularly satisfying
on both sides. Separate as their interests seemed, those of the
French country-priest, and of the Englishman of letters, famous
already in his own department, they had, nevertheless, much
community of feeling apart from their common affection for a
child. Now, for many years, he had been established in their
good graces, so that it had become an habit with him to spend his
holiday—it was often a very extended one—at Ploumariel ;
while to the Letêtres, as well as to Marie-Ursule herself, this
annual sojourn of Campion's had become the occasion of the year,
the one event which pleasantly relieved the monotony of life in
this remote village ; though that, too, was a not unpleasant routine.
Insensibly Campion had come to find his chief pleasure in consideration of this child of an old friend, whose gradual growth
beneath influences which seemed to him singularly exquisite and
fine, he had watched so long ; whose future, now that her childhood, her schooldays at the convent had come to an end, threatened
to occupy him with an anxiety more intimate than any which
hitherto he had known. Marie-Ursule's future ! They had
talked much of it that summer, the priest and the Englishman,
who accompanied him in his long morning walks, through green
lanes, and over white, dusty roads, and past fields perfumed with
                                                                    the

the pungently pleasant smell of the blood-red *sarrasin*, when he paid visits to the sick who lived on the outskirts of his scattered parish. Campion became aware then of an increasing difficulty in discussing this matter impersonally, in the impartial manner becoming a guardian. Odd thrills of jealousy stirred within him when he was asked to contemplate Marie-Ursule's possible suitors. And yet, it was with a very genuine surprise, at least for the moment, that he met the Curé's sudden pressing home of a more personal contingency—he took this freedom of an old friend with a shrewd twinkle in his eye, which suggested that all along this had been chiefly in his mind. "*Mon bon ami*, why should you not marry her yourself? That would please all of us so much." And he insisted, with kindly insistence, on the propriety of the thing : dwelling on Campion's established position, their long habit of friendship, his own and his sister's confidence and esteem, taking for granted, with that sure insight which is the gift of many women and of most priests, that on the ground of affection alone the justification was too obvious to be pressed. And he finished with a smile, stopping to take a pinch of snuff with a sigh of relief— the relief of a man who has at least seasonably unburdened himself.

"Surely, *mon ami*, some such possibility must have been in your mind ? "

Campion hesitated for a moment ; then he proffered his hand, which the other warmly grasped. "You read me aright," he said slowly, "only I hardly realised it before. Even now—no, how can I believe it possible—that she should care for me. *Non sum dignus, non sum dignus.* Consider her youth, her inexperience ; the best part of my life is behind me."

But the Curé smiled reassuringly. "The best part is before you, Campion ; you have the heart of a boy. Do we not know
you ?

you ?　And for the child—rest tranquil there !　I have the word o
my sister, who is a wise woman, that she is sincerely attached t
you ; not to speak of the evidence of my own eyes.　She will b
seventeen shortly, then she can speak for herself.　And to whon
else can we trust her ? "

The shadow of these confidences hung over Campion when h
next saw Marie-Ursule, and troubled him vaguely during th
remainder of his visit, which this year, indeed, he considerabl
curtailed.　Inevitably he was thrown much with the young gir
and if daily the charm which he found in her presence wa
sensibly increased, as he studied her from a fresh point of view, h
was none the less disquieted at the part which he might be calle
upon to play.　Diffident and scrupulous, a shy man, knowin
little of women ; and at least by temperament, a sad man, h
trembled before felicity, as many at the palpable breath of mis
fortune.　And his difficulty was increased by the conviction
forced upon him irresistibly, little as he could accuse himself o
vanity, that the decision rested with himself.　Her liking for hin
was genuine and deep, her confidence implicit.　He had but t
ask her and she would place her hand in his and go forth wit
him, as trustfully as a child.　And when they came to celebrat
her *fête*, Marie-Ursule's seventeenth birthday—it occurred a littl
before the Assumption—it was almost disinterestedly that he ha
determined upon his course.　At least it was security which h
could promise her, as a younger man might not ; a constant an
single-minded kindness ; a devotion not the less valuable, becaus
it was mature and reticent, lacking, perhaps, the jealous ardours o
youth.　Nevertheless, he was going back to England withou
having revealed himself ; there should be no unseasonable haste i
the matter ; he would give her another year.　The Curé smile
deprecatingly at the procrastination ; but on this point Campio
wa

was firm. And on this, his last evening, he spoke only of trivial things to Marie-Ursule, as they sat presently over the tea—a mild and flavourless beverage—which the young girl had prepared. Yet he noticed later, after their early supper, when she strolled up with him to the hill overlooking the village, a certain new shyness in her manner, a shadow, half timid, half expectant in her clear eyes which permitted him to believe that she was partly prepared. When they reached the summit, stood clear of the pine trees by an ancient stone Calvary, Ploumariel lay below them, very fair in the light of the setting sun ; and they stopped to rest themselves, to admire.

"Ploumariel is very beautiful," said Campion after a while. "Ah ! Marie-Ursule, you are fortunate to be here."

"Yes." She accepted his statement simply, then suddenly : "You should not go away." He smiled, his eyes turning from the village in the valley to rest upon her face : after all, she was the daintiest picture, and Ploumariel with its tall slate roofs, its sleeping houses, her appropriate frame.

"I shall come back, I shall come back," he murmured. She had gathered a bunch of ruddy heather as they walked, and her fingers played with it now nervously. Campion stretched out his hand for it. She gave it him without a word.

"I will take it with me to London," he said ; "I will have Morbihan in my rooms."

"It will remind you—make you think of us sometimes ? "

For answer he could only touch her hand lightly with his lips. "Do you think that was necessary ? " And they resumed their homeward way silently, although to both of them the air seemed heavy with unspoken words.

When

III

When he was in London—and it was in London that for nir
months out of the twelve Benedict Campion was to be found—h
lived in the Temple, at the top of Hare Court, in the very sam
rooms in which he had installed himself, years ago, when he gav
up his Oxford fellowship, electing to follow the profession o
letters. Returning there from Ploumariel, he resumed at onc
easily, his old avocations. He had always been a secluded ma
living chiefly in books and in the past ; but this year he seeme
less than ever inclined to knock at the hospitable doors which we
open to him. For in spite of his reserve, his diffidence, Campion
success might have been social, had he cared for it, and not purel
academic. His had come to be a name in letters, in the high
paths of criticism ; and he had made no enemies. To his succes
indeed, gradual and quiet as this was, he had never grown quit
accustomed, contrasting the little he had actually achieved with a
that he had desired to do. His original work was of the slightes
and a book that was in his head he had never found time to writ
His name was known in other ways, as a man of ripe knowledg
of impeccable taste ; as a born editor of choice reprints, o
inaccessible classics : above all, as an authority—the greatest, upo
the literature and the life (its flavour at once courtly, an
mystical, had to him an unique charm) of the seventeenth century
His heart was in that age, and from much lingering over it, h
had come to view modern life with a curious detachment, a sens
of remote hostility : Democracy, the Salvation Army, the novels o
M. Zola—he disliked them all impartially. A Catholic by lon
inheritance, he held his religion for something more than a
heirloom

heirloom ; he exhaled it, like an intimate quality ; his mind being essentially of that kind to which a mystical view of things comes easiest.

This year passed with him much as any other of the last ten years had passed ; at least the routine of his daily existence admitted little outward change. And yet inwardly, he was conscious of alteration, of a certain quiet illumination which was a new thing to him.

Although at Ploumariel when the prospect of such a marriage had dawned on him, his first impression had been one of strangeness, he could reflect now that it was some such possibility as this which he had always kept vaguely in view. He had prided himself upon few things more than his patience ; and now it appeared that this was to be rewarded ; he was glad that he had known how to wait. This girl, Marie-Ursule, had an immense personal charm for him, but, beyond that, she was representative—her traditions were exactly those which the ideal girl of Campion's imagination would possess. She was not only personally adorable; she was also generically of the type which he admired. It was possibly because this type was, after all, so rare, that looking back, Campion in his middle age, could drag out of the recesses of his memory no spectre to compete with her. She was his first love precisely because the conditions, so choice and admirable, which rendered it inevitable for him to love her, had never occurred before. And he could watch the time of his probation gliding away with a pleased expectancy which contained no alloy of impatience. An illumination—a quite tranquil illumination : yes, it was under some such figure, without heart-burning, or adolescent fever, that love as it came to Campion was best expressed. Yet if this love was lucent rather than turbulent, that it was also deep he could remind himself, when a letter from the priest, while the spring was yet young, had sent him to Brittany, a month

or

or two before his accustomed time, with an anxiety that was not solely due to bewilderment.

"*Our child is well, mon bon,*" so he wrote. "*Do not alarm yourself. But it will be good for you to come, if it be only because of an idea she has, that you may remove. An idea! Call it rather a fancy—at least your coming will dispel it. Petites entêtées: I have no patience with these mystical little girls.*"

His musings on the phrase, with its interpretation varying to his mood, lengthened his long sea-passage, and the interminable leagues of railway which separated him from Pontivy, whence he had still some twenty miles to travel by the *Courrier*, before he reached his destination. But at Pontivy, the round, ruddy face of M. Letêtre greeting him on the platform dispelled any serious misgiving. Outside the post-office the familiar conveyance awaited them: its yellow inscription "Pontivy-Ploumariel," touched Campion electrically, as did the cheery greeting of the driver, which was that of an old friend. They shared the interior of the rusty trap—a fossil among vehicles—they chanced to be the only travellers, and to the accompaniment of jingling harness, and the clattering hoofs of the brisk little Carhaix horses, M. Letêtre explained himself.

"A vocation, *mon Dieu!* if all the little girls who fancied themselves with one, were to have their way, to whom would our poor France look for children? They are good women, *nos Ursulines*, ah, yes; but our Marie-Ursule is a good child, and blessed matrimony also is a sacrament. You shall talk to her, my Campion. It is a little fancy, you see, such as will come to young girls; a convent ague, but when she sees you" . . . He took snuff with emphasis, and flipped his broad fingers suggestively. "*Craque!* it is a betrothal, and a *trousseau*, and not the habit of religion, that Mademoiselle is full of. You will talk to her?"

Campion

Campion assented silently, absently, his eyes had wandered away, and looked through the little square of window at the sad-coloured Breton country, at the rows of tall poplars, which guarded the miles of dusty road like sombre sentinels. And the priest with a reassured air pulled out his breviary, and began to say his office in an imperceptible undertone. After a while he crossed himself, shut the book, and pillowing his head against the hot, shiny leather of the carriage, sought repose ; very soon his regular, stertorous breathing, assured his companion that he was asleep. Campion closed his eyes also, not indeed in search of slumber, though he was travel weary ; rather the better to isolate himself with the perplexity of his own thoughts. An indefinable sadness invaded him, and he could envy the priest's simple logic, which gave such short shrift to obstacles that Campion, with his subtle melancholy, which made life to him almost morbidly an affair of fine shades and nice distinctions, might easily exaggerate.

Of the two, perhaps the priest had really the more secular mind, as it certainly excelled Campion's in that practical wisdom, or common sense, which may be of more avail than subtlety in the mere economy of life. And what to the Curé was a simple matter enough, the removal of the idle fancy of a girl, might be to Campion, in his scrupulous temper, and his overweening tenderness towards just those pieties and renunciations which such a fancy implied, a task to be undertaken hardly with relish, perhaps without any real conviction, deeply as his personal wishes might be implicated in success. And the heart had gone out of his journey long before a turn of the road brought them in sight of Ploumariel.

Up

IV

Up by the great, stone Calvary, where they had climbed nearly a year before, Campion stood, his face deliberately averted, while the young girl uttered her hesitating confidences ; hesitating, yet candid, with a candour which seemed to separate him from the child by more than a measurable space of years, to set him with an appealing trustfulness in the seat of judgment—for him, for her. They had wandered there insensibly, through apple-orchards white with the promise of a bountiful harvest, and up the pine-clad hill, talking of little things—trifles to beguile their way—perhaps, in a sort of vain procrastination.   Once, Marie-Ursule had plucked a branch of the snowy blossom, and he had playfully chided her that the cider would be less by a *litre* that year in Brittany. " But the blossom is so much prettier," she protested ; " and there will be apples and apples—always enough apples.   But I like the blossom best—and it is so soon over."

And then, emerging clear of the trees, with Ploumariel lying in its quietude in the serene sunshine below them, a sudden strenuousness had supervened, and the girl had unburdened herself, speaking tremulously, quickly, in an undertone almost passionate ; and Campion, perforce, had listened. . . . A fancy ? a whim ?   Yes, he reflected ; to the normal, entirely healthy mind, any choice of exceptional conditions, any special self-consecration or withdrawal from the common lot of men and women must draw down upon it some such reproach, seeming the mere pedantry of inexperience. Yet, against his reason, and what he would fain call his better judgment, something in his heart of hearts stirred sympathetically with this notion of the girl.   And it was no fixed resolution, no

deliberate

deliberate justification which she pleaded. She was soft, and pliable, and even her plea for renunciation contained pretty, feminine inconsequences ; and it touched Campion strangely. Argument he could have met with argument ; an ardent conviction he might have assailed with pleading ; but that note of appeal in her pathetic young voice, for advice, for sympathy, disarmed him.

"Yet the world," he protested at last, but half-heartedly, with a sense of self-imposture : "the world, Marie-Ursule, it has its disappointments ; but there are compensations."

"I am afraid, afraid," she murmured.

Their eyes alike sought instinctively the Convent of the Ursulines, white and sequestered in the valley—a visible symbol of security, of peace, perhaps of happiness.

"Even there they have their bad days : do not doubt it."

"But nothing happens," she said simply ; "one day is like another. They can never be very sad, you know."

They were silent for a time: the girl, shading her eyes with one small white hand, continued to regard the convent ; and Campion considered her fondly.

"What can I say ? " he exclaimed at last. "What would you put on me ? Your uncle—he is a priest—surely the most natural adviser—you know his wishes."

She shook her head. "With him it is different—I am one of his family—he is not a priest for me. And he considers me a little girl—and yet I am old enough to marry. Many young girls have had a vocation before my age. Ah, help me, decide for me ! " she pleaded ; "you are my *tuteur*."

"And a very old friend, Marie-Ursule." He smiled rather sadly. Last year seemed so long ago, and the word, which he had almost spoken then, was no longer seasonable. A note in his
voice,

voice, inexplicable, might have touched her. She took his hand impulsively, but he withdrew it quickly, as though her touch had scalded him.

"You look very tired ; you are not used to our Breton rambles in this sun. See, I will run down to the cottage by the chapel and fetch you some milk. Then you shall tell me."

When he was alone the smile faded from his face and was succeeded by a look of lassitude, as he sat himself beneath the shadow of the Calvary to wrestle with his responsibility. Perhaps it was a vocation : the phrase, sounding strangely on modern ears, to him, at least, was no anachronism. Women of his race, from generation to generation, had heard some such voice and had obeyed it. That it went unheeded now was, perhaps, less a proof that it was silent, than that people had grown hard and deaf, in a world that had deteriorated. Certainly the convent had to him no vulgar, Protestant significance, to be combated for its intrinsic barbarism ; it suggested nothing cold nor narrow nor mean, was veritably a gracious choice, a generous effort after perfection. Then it was for his own sake, on an egoistic impulse, that he should dissuade her ? And it rested with him ; he had no doubt that he could mould her, even yet, to his purpose. The child ! how he loved her. . . . But would it ever be quite the same with them after that morning ? Or must there be henceforth a shadow between them ; the knowledge of something missed, of the lower end pursued, the higher slighted ? Yet, if she loved him ? He let his head drop on his hands, murmured aloud at the hard chance which made him at once judge and advocate in his own cause. He was not conscious of praying, but his mind fell into that condition of aching blankness which is, perhaps, an extreme prayer. Presently he looked down again at Ploumariel, with its coronal of faint smoke ascending in the
perfectly

perfectly still air, at the white convent of the Dames Ursulines, which seemed to dominate and protect it. How peaceful it was! And his thought wandered to London : to its bustle and noise, its squalid streets, to his life there, to its literary coteries, its politics, its society ; vulgar and trivial and sordid they all seemed from this point of vantage. That was the world he had pleaded for, and it was into that he would bring the child. . . . And suddenly, with a strange reaction, he was seized with a sense of the wisdom of her choice, its pictorial fitness, its benefit for both of them. He felt at once and finally, that he acquiesced in it ; that any other ending to his love had been an impossible grossness, and that to lose her in just that fashion was the only way in which he could keep her always. And his acquiescence was without bitterness, and attended only by that indefinable sadness which to a man of his temper was but the last refinement of pleasure. He had renounced, but he had triumphed ; for it seemed to him that his renunciation would be an ægis to him always against the sordid facts of life, a protest against the vulgarity of instinct, the tyranny of institutions. And he thought of the girl's life, as it should be, with a tender appreciation—as of something precious laid away in lavender. He looked up to find her waiting before him with a basin half full of milk, warm still, fresh from the cow ; and she watched him in silence while he drank. Then their eyes met, and she gave a little cry.

"You will help me ? Ah, I see that you will ! And you think I am right ? "

"I think you are right, Marie-Ursule."

"And you will persuade my uncle ? "

"I will persuade him."

She took his hand in silence, and they stood so for a minute, gravely regarding each other. Then they prepared to descend.

Night Piece

By Aubrey Beardsley

Reproduced by the Swan Electric Engraving Company

Stella Maris

By Arthur Symons

WHY is it I remember yet
    You, of all women one has met
In random wayfare, as one meets
The chance romances of the streets,
The Juliet of a night ?   I know
Your heart holds many a Romeo.
And I, who call to mind your face
In so serene a pausing-place,
Where the bright pure expanse of sea,
The shadowy shore's austerity,
Seems a reproach to you and me,
I too have sought on many a breast
The ecstasy of love's unrest,
I too have had my dreams, and met
(Ah me !) how many a Juliet.
Why is it, then, that I recall
You, neither first nor last of all ?
For, surely as I see to-night
The glancing of the lighthouse light,
Against the sky, across the bay,
As turn by turn it falls my way,

So

So surely do I see your eyes
Out of the empty night arise,
Child, you arise and smile to me
Out of the night, out of the sea,
The Nereid of a moment there,
And is it seaweed in your hair?

O lost and wrecked, how long ago,
Out of the drowned past, I know,
You come to call me, come to claim
My share of your delicious shame.
Child, I remember, and can tell
One night we loved each other well;
And one night's love, at least or most,
Is not so small a thing to boast.
You were adorable, and I
Adored you to infinity,
That nuptial night too briefly borne
To the oblivion of morn.
Oh, no oblivion! for I feel
Your lips deliriously steal
Along my neck, and fasten there;
I feel the perfume of your hair,
And your soft breast that heaves and dips,
Desiring my desirous lips,
And that ineffable delight
When souls turn bodies, and unite
In the intolerable, the whole
Rapture of the embodied soul.

That joy was ours, we passed it by;
You have forgotten me, and I

                                    Rememb

Remember you thus strangely, won
An instant from oblivion.
And I, remembering, would declare
That joy, not shame, is ours to share,
Joy that we had the will and power,
In spite of fate, to snatch one hour,
Out of vague nights, and days at strife,
So infinitely full of life.
And 'tis for this I see you rise,
A wraith, with starlight in your eyes,
Here, where the drowsy-minded mood
Is one with Nature's solitude ;
For this, for this, you come to me
Out of the night, out of the sea.

The Foolish Virgin

By George Gissi

C OMING down to breakfast, as usual, rather late, Miss Jew
was surprised to find several persons still at table. Th
conversation ceased as she entered, and all eyes were directed
her with a look in which she discerned some special meani
For several reasons she was in an irritable humour ; the significa
smiles, the subdued " Good mornings," and the silence that f
lowed, so jarred upon her nerves that, save for curiosity, she wou
have turned and left the room.

Mrs. Banting (generally at this hour busy in other parts of t
house) inquired with a sympathetic air whether she would ta
porridge ; the others awaited her reply as if it were a matter
general interest. Miss Jewell abruptly demanded an egg. T
awkward pause was broken by a high falsetto.

" I believe you know who it is all the time, Mr. Drake," sa
Miss Ayres, addressing the one man present.

" I assure you I don't. Upon my word, I don't. The wh
thing astonishes me."

Resolutely silent, Miss Jewell listened to a conversation t
drift of which remained dark to her, until some one spoke the na
" Mr. Cheeseman ; " then it was with difficulty that she controll
her face and her tongue. The servant brought her an egg. S
stru

truck it clumsily with the edge of the spoon, and asked in an
ffected drawl :

"What are you people talking about ? "

Mrs. Sleath, smiling maliciously, took it upon herself to
eply.

"Mr. Drake has had a letter from Mr. Cheeseman. He writes
hat he's engaged, but doesn't say who to. Delicious mystery,
n't it ? "

The listener tried to swallow a piece of bread-and-butter, and
eemed to struggle with a constriction of the throat. Then, look-
ng round the table, she said with contemptuous pleasantry :

"Some lodging-house servant, I shouldn't wonder."

Every one laughed. Then Mr. Drake declared he must be off
nd rose from the table. The ladies also moved, and in a minute
r two Miss Jewell sat at her breakfast alone.

She was a tall, slim person, with unremarkable, not ill-moulded
eatures. Nature meant her to be graceful in form and pleasantly
eminine of countenance ; unwholesome habit of mind and body
vas responsible for the defects that now appeared in her. She had
o colour, no flesh ; but an agreeable smile would well have
ecome her lips, and her eyes needed only the illumination of
ealthy thought to be more than commonly attractive. A few
nonths would see the close of her twenty-ninth year ; but Mrs.
anting's boarders, with some excuse, judged her on the wrong
ide of thirty.

Her meal, a sad pretence, was soon finished. She went to the
vindow and stood there for five minutes looking at the cabs and
edestrians in the sunny street. Then, with the languid step
vhich had become natural to her, she ascended the stairs and
urned into the drawing-room. Here, as she had expected, two
adies sat in close conversation. Without heeding them, she
                                                        walked

walked to the piano, selected a sheet of music, and sat down t
play.

Presently, whilst she drummed with vigour on the keys, som
one approached ; she looked up and saw Mrs. Banting ; the othe
persons had left the room.

" If it's true," murmured Mrs. Banting, with genuine kindl
ness on her flabby lips, " all I can say is that it's shameful—shame
ful ! "

Miss Jewell stared at her.

" What do you mean ? "

" Mr. Cheeseman—to go and——"

" I don't understand you. What is it to me ? "

The words were thrown out almost fiercely, and a crash on th
piano drowned whatever Mrs. Banting meant to utter in repl
Miss Jewell now had the drawing-room to herself.

She " practised " for half an hour, careering through many fam
liar pieces with frequent mechanical correction of time-honoure
blunders. When at length she was going up to her room,
grinning servant handed her a letter which had just arrive
A glance at the envelope told her from whom it came, an
in privacy she at once opened it. The writer's address w
Glasgow.

" My dear Rosamund," began the letter, " I can't understan
why you write in such a nasty way. For some time now you
letters have been horrid. I don't show them to William becaus
if I did he would get into a tantrum. What I have to say to yo
now is this, that we simply can't go on sending you the mone
We haven't it to spare, and that's the plain truth. You thi
we're rolling in money, and it's no use telling you we are no
William said last night that you *must* find some way of supportir
yourself, and I can only say the same. You are a lady and had

thoroug

thorough good education, and I am sure you have only to exert yourself. William says I may promise you a five-pound note twice a year, but more than that you must not expect. Now do just think over your position——"

She threw the sheet of paper aside, and sat down to brood miserably. This little back bedroom, at no time conducive to good spirits, had seen Rosamund in many a dreary or exasperated mood ; to-day it beheld her on the very verge of despair. Illuminated texts of Scripture spoke to her from the walls in vain ; portraits of admired clergymen smiled vainly from the mantelpiece. She was conscious only of a dirty carpet, an ill-made bed, faded curtains, and a window that looked out on nothing. One cannot expect much for a guinea a week, when it includes board and lodging ; the bedroom was at least a refuge, but even that, it seemed, would henceforth be denied her. Oh, the selfishness of people ! And oh, the perfidy of man !

For eight years, since the breaking up of her home, Rosamund had lived in London boarding-houses. To begin with, she could count on a sufficient income, resulting from property in which she had a legitimate share. Owing to various causes, the value of this property had steadily diminished, until at length she became dependent upon the subsidies of kinsfolk ; for more than a twelve-month now, the only person able and willing to continue such remittances had been her married sister, and Rosamund had hardly known what it was to have a shilling of pocket-money. From time to time she thought feebly and confusedly of " doing something," but her aims were so vague, her capabilities so inadequate, that she always threw aside the intention in sheer hopelessness. Whatever will she might once have possessed had evaporated in the boarding-house atmosphere. It was hard to believe that her brother-in-law would ever withhold the poor five pounds a month.
And

And—what is the use of boarding-houses if not to renew indefi-
nitely the hope of marriage ?

She was not of the base order of women. Conscience yet lived
in her, and drew support from religion ; something of modesty,
of self-respect, still clad her starving soul. Ignorance and ill-luck
had once or twice thrown her into such society as may be found
in establishments outwardly respectable ; she trembled and fled.
Even in such a house as this of Mrs. Banting's, she had known
sickness of disgust. Herself included, four single women abode
here at the present time ; and the scarcely disguised purpose of
every one of them was to entrap a marriageable man. In the
others, it seemed to her detestable, and she hated all three, even as
they in their turn detested her. Rosamund flattered herself with
the persuasion that she did not aim merely at marriage and a sub-
sistence ; she would not marry *any* one ; her desire was for sympathy, true companionship. In years gone by she had used to
herself a more sacred word ; nowadays the homely solace seemed
enough. And of late a ray of hope had glimmered upon her dusty
path. Mr. Cheeseman, with his plausible airs, his engaging smile,
had won something more than her confidence ; an acquaintance
of six months, ripening at length to intimacy, justified her in
regarding him with sanguine emotion. They had walked together in Kensington Gardens ; they had exchanged furtive and
significant glances at table and elsewhere ; every one grew aware
of the mutual preference. It shook her with a painful misgiving
when Mr. Cheeseman went away for his holiday and spoke no
word ; but probably he would write. He had written—to his
friend Drake ; and all was over.

Her affections suffered, but that was not the worst. Her pride
had never received so cruel a blow.

After a life of degradation which might well have unsexed her,
                                                           Rosamund

Rosamund remained a woman. The practice of affectations numberless had taught her one truth, that she could never hope to charm save by reliance upon her feminine qualities. Boarding-house girls, such numbers of whom she had observed, seemed all intent upon disowning their womanhood; they cultivated masculine habits, wore as far as possible male attire, talked loud slang, threw scorn (among themselves at all events) upon domestic virtues; and not a few of them seemed to profit by the prevailing fashion. Rosamund had tried these tactics, always with conscious failure. At other times, and vastly to her relief, she aimed in precisely the opposite direction, encouraging herself in feminine extremes. She would talk with babbling *naïveté*, exaggerate the languor induced by idleness, lack of exercise, and consequent ill-health; betray timidities and pruderies, let fall a pious phrase, rise of a morning for " early celebration " and let the fact be known. These and the like extravagances had appeared to fascinate Mr. Cheeseman, who openly professed his dislike for androgynous persons. And Rosamund enjoyed the satisfaction of moderate sincerity. Thus, or very much in this way, would she be content to live. Romantic passion she felt to be beyond her scope. Long ago—ah! perhaps long ago, when she first knew Geoffrey Hunt——

The name, as it crossed her mind, suggested an escape from the insufferable *ennui* and humiliation of hours till evening. It must be half a year since she called upon the Hunts, her only estimable acquaintances in or near London. They lived at Teddington, and the railway fare was always a deterrent; nor did she care much for Mrs. Hunt and her daughters, who of late years had grown reserved with her, as if uneasy about her mode of life. True, they were not at all snobbish; homely, though well-to-do people; but they had such strict views, and could not understand

the

the existence of a woman less energetic than themselves. In her present straits, which could hardly be worse, their counsel might prove of value ; though she doubted her courage when it came to making confessions.

She would do without luncheon (impossible to sit at table with those " creatures ") and hope to make up for it at tea ; in truth appetite was not likely to trouble her. Then for dress. Wearily she compared this garment with that, knowing beforehand that all were out of fashion and more or less shabby. Oh, what did it matter ! She had come to beggary, the result that might have been foreseen long ago. Her faded costume suited fitly enough with her fortunes—nay, with her face. For just then she caught a sight of herself in the glass, and shrank. A lump choked her : looking desperately, as if for help, for pity, through gathering tears, she saw the Bible verse on the nearest wall : " Come unto me——" Her heart became that of a woful child ; she put her hands before her face, and prayed in the old, simple words of childhood.

As her call must not be made before half-past three, she could not set out upon the journey forthwith ; but it was a relief to get away from the house. In this bright weather, Kensington Gardens, not far away, seemed a natural place for loitering, but the alleys would remind her too vividly of late companionship ; she walked in another direction, sauntered for an hour by the shop windows of Westbourne Grove, and, when she felt tired, sat at the railway station until it was time to start. At Teddington, half a mile's walk lay before her ; though she felt no hunger, long abstinence and the sun's heat taxed her strength to the point of exhaustion ; on reaching her friend's door, she stood trembling with nervousness and fatigue. The door opened, and to her dismay she learnt that Mrs. Hunt was away from home.

Happily,

Happily, the servant added that Miss Caroline was in the garden.

"I'll go round," said Rosamund at once.   "Don't trouble——"

The pathway round the pleasant little house soon brought her within view of a young lady who sat in a garden-chair, sewing. But Miss Caroline was not alone ; near to her stood a man in shirt-sleeves and bare-headed, vigorously sawing a plank ; he seemed to be engaged in the construction of a summer-house, and Rosamund took him at first sight for a mechanic, but when he turned round, exhibiting a ruddy face all agleam with health and good humour, she recognised the young lady's brother, Geoffrey Hunt. He, as though for the moment puzzled, looked fixedly at her.

"Oh, Miss Jewell, how glad I am to see you !"

Enlightened by his sister's words, Geoffrey dropped the saw, and stepped forward with still heartier greeting. Had civility permitted, he might easily have explained his doubts. It was some six years since his last meeting with Rosamund, and she had changed not a little ; he remembered her as a graceful and rather pretty girl, with life in her, even if it ran for the most part to silliness, gaily dressed, sprightly of manner ; notwithstanding the account he had received of her from his relatives, it astonished him to look upon this limp, faded woman. In Rosamund's eyes, Geoffrey was his old self ; perhaps a trifle more stalwart, and if anything handsomer, but with just the same light in his eyes, the same smile on his bearded face, the same cordiality of utterance. For an instant, she compared him with Mr. Cheeseman, and flushed for very shame. Unable to command her voice, she stammered incoherent nothings ; only when a seat supported her weary body did she lose the dizziness which had threatened downright collapse ; then she closed her eyes, and forgot everything but the sense of rest.

Geoffrey

Geoffrey drew on his coat, and spoke jestingly of his amateur workmanship. Such employment, however, seemed not inappropriate to him, for his business was that of a timber-merchant. Of late years he had lived abroad, for the most part in Canada. Rosamund learnt that at present he was having a longish holiday.

"And you go back to Canada?"

This she asked when Miss Hunt had stepped into the house to call for tea. Geoffrey answered that it was doubtful; for various reasons he rather hoped to remain in England, but the choice did not altogether rest with him.

"At all events"—she gave a poor little laugh—"you haven't pined in exile."

"Not a bit of it. I have always had plenty of hard work—the one thing needful."

"Yes—I remember—you always used to say that. And I used to protest. You granted, I think, that it might be different with women."

"Did I?"

He wished to add something to the point, but refrained out of compassion. It was clear to him that Miss Jewell, at all events, would have been none the worse for exacting employment. Mrs. Hunt had spoken of her with the disapprobation natural in a healthy, active woman of the old school, and Geoffrey himself could not avoid a contemptuous judgment.

"You have lived in London all this time?" he asked, before she could speak.

"Yes. Where else should I live? My sister at Glasgow doesn't want me there, and—and there's nobody else, you know." She tried to laugh. "I have friends in London—well, that is to say—at all events I'm not *quite* solitary."

The man smiled, and could not allow her to suspect how profoundly

foundly he pitied such a condition. Caroline Hunt had reappeared ; she began to talk of her mother and sister, who were enjoying themselves in Wales. Her own holiday would come upon their return ; Geoffrey was going to take her to Switzerland.

Tea arrived just as Rosamund was again sinking into bodily faintness and desolation of spirit. It presently restored her, but she could hardly converse. She kept hoping that Caroline would offer her some invitation—to lunch, to dine, anything ; but as yet no such thought seemed to occur to the young hostess. Suddenly the aspect of things was altered by the arrival of new callers, a whole family, man, wife and three children, strangers to Rosamund. For a time it seemed as if she must go away without any kind of solace ; for Geoffrey had quitted her, and she sat alone. On the spur of irrational resentment, she rose and advanced to Miss Hunt.

"Oh, but you are not going ! I want you to stay and have dinner with us, if you can. Would it make you too late ? "

Rosamund flushed and could scarce contain her delight. In a moment she was playing with the youngest of the children, and even laughing aloud, so that Geoffrey glanced curiously towards her. Even the opportunity of private conversation which she had not dared to count upon was granted before long; when the callers had departed Caroline excused herself, and left her brother alone with the guest for half an hour. There was no time to be lost ; Rosamund broached almost immediately the subject uppermost in her mind.

"Mr. Hunt, I know how dreadful it is to have people asking for advice, but if I *might*—if you could have patience with me——"

"I haven't much wisdom to spare," he answered, with easy good-nature.

"Oh,

"Oh, you are very rich in it, compared with poor me.—And my position is *so* difficult. I want—I am trying to find some way of being useful in the world. I am tired of living for myself. I seem to be such a useless creature. Surely even *I* must have *some* talent, which it's my duty to put to use! Where should I turn? Could you help me with a suggestion?"

Her words, now that she had overcome the difficulty of beginning, chased each other with breathless speed, and Geoffrey was all but constrained to seriousness; he took it for granted, however, that Miss Jewell frequently used this language; doubtless it was part of her foolish, futile existence to talk of her soul's welfare, especially in *tête-à-tête* with unmarried men. The truth he did not suspect, and Rosamund could not bring herself to convey it in plain words.

"I do so envy the people who have something to live for!" Thus she panted. "I fear I have *never* had a purpose in life—I'm sure I don't know why. Of course I'm only a woman, but even women nowadays are doing so much. You don't despise their efforts, do you?"

"Not indiscriminately."

"If I could feel myself a profitable member of society!—I want to be lifted above my wretched self. Is there no great end to which I could devote myself?"

Her phrases grew only more magniloquent, and all the time she was longing for courage to say: "How can I earn money?" Geoffrey, confirmed in the suspicion that she talked only for effect, indulged his natural humour.

"I'm such a groveller, Miss Jewell. I never knew these aspirations. I see the world mainly as cubic feet of timber."

"No, no, you won't make me believe that. I *know* you have ideals!"

"That

"That word reminds me of poor old Halliday. You remember Halliday, don't you?"

In vexed silence, Rosamund shook her head.

"But I think you must have met him, in the old days. A tall, fair man—no? He talked a great deal about ideals, and meant to move the world. We lost sight of each other when I first left England, and only met again a day or two ago. He is married, and has three children, and looks fifty years old, though he can't be much more than thirty. He took me to see his wife —they live at Forest Hill."

Rosamund was not listening, and the speaker became aware of it. Having a purpose in what he was about to say, he gently claimed her attention.

"I think Mrs. Halliday is the kind of woman who would interest you. If ever any one had a purpose in life, *she* has."

"Indeed? And what?"

"To keep house admirably, and bring up her children as well as possible, on an income which would hardly supply some women with shoe-leather."

"Oh, that's very dreadful!"

"Very fine, it seems to me. I never saw a woman for whom I could feel more respect. Halliday and she suit each other perfectly; they would be the happiest people in England if they had any money. As he walked back with me to the station he talked about their difficulties. They can't afford to engage a good servant (if one exists nowadays), and cheap sluts have driven them frantic, so that Mrs. Halliday does everything with her own hands."

"It must be awful."

"Pretty hard, no doubt. She is an educated woman—otherwise, of course, she couldn't, and wouldn't, manage it. And, by-the-

bye

bye "—he paused for quiet emphasis—" she has a sister, unmarried, who lives in the country and does nothing at all. It occurs to one—doesn't it ?—that the idle sister might pretty easily find scope for *her* energies."

Rosamund stared at the ground. She was not so dull as to lose the significance of this story, and she imagined that Geoffrey reflected upon herself in relation to her own sister. She broke the long silence by saying awkwardly :

" I'm sure *I* would never allow a sister of mine to lead such a life."

" I don't think you would," replied the other. And, though he spoke genially, Rosamund felt it a very moderate declaration of his belief in her. Overcome by strong feeling, she exclaimed :

" I would do *anything* to be of use in the world. You don't think I mean it, but I do, Mr. Hunt. I——"

Her voice faltered ; the all-important word stuck in her throat. And at that moment Geoffrey rose.

" Shall we walk about ?   Let me show you my mother's fernery she is very proud of it."

That was the end of intimate dialogue. Rosamund felt aggrieved, and tried to shape sarcasms, but the man's imperturbable good-humour soon made her forget everything save the pleasure of being in his company. It was a bitter-sweet evening, yet perhaps enjoyment predominated. Of course, Geoffrey would conduct her to the station ; she never lost sight of this hope. There would be another opportunity for plain speech. But her desire was frustrated ; at the time of departure, Caroline said that they might as well all go together. Rosamund could have wept for chagrin.

She returned to the detested house, the hateful little bedroom, and there let her tears have way. In dread lest the hysterical sobs should be overheard, she all but stifled herself.

Then,

Then, as if by blessed inspiration, a great thought took shape in her despairing mind. At the still hour of night she suddenly sat up in the darkness, which seemed illumined by a wondrous hope. A few minutes motionless ; the mental light grew dazzling ; she sprang out of bed, partly dressed herself, and by the rays of a candle sat down to write a letter :

" Dear Mr. Hunt,

"Yesterday I did not tell you the whole truth. I have nothing to live upon, and I *must* find employment or starve. My brother-in-law has been supporting me for a long time—I am ashamed to tell you, but I *will*, and he can do so no longer. I wanted to ask you for practical advice, but I did not make my meaning clear. For all that, you *did* advise me, and very well indeed. I wish to offer myself as domestic help to poor Mrs. Halliday. Do you think she would have me ? I ask no wages—only food and lodging. I will work harder and better than any general servants—I *will indeed*. My health is not bad, and I am fairly strong. Don't—don't throw scorn on this ! Will you recommend me to Mrs. Halliday—or ask Mrs. Hunt to do so ? I beg that you will. Please write to me at once, and say yes. I shall be ever grateful to you.

" Very sincerely yours,

" Rosamund Jewell."

This she posted as early as possible. The agonies she endured in waiting for a reply served to make her heedless of boarding-house spite, and by the last post that same evening came Geoffrey's letter. He wrote that her suggestion was startling. "Your motive seems to me very praiseworthy, but whether the thing would be possible is another question. I dare not take upon myself the responsibility of counselling you to such a step. Pray, take time, and think. I am most grieved to hear of your difficulties, but is there not some better way out of them ? "

Yes,

Yes, there it was! Geoffrey Hunt could not believe in her power to *do* anything praiseworthy. So had it been six years ago, when she would have gone through flood and flame to win his admiration. But in those days she was a girlish simpleton; she had behaved idiotically. It should be different now; were it at the end of her life, she would prove to him that he had slighted her unjustly!

Brave words, but Rosamund attached some meaning to them. The woman in her—the ever-prevailing woman—was wrought by fears and vanities, urgencies and desires, to a strange point of exaltation. Forthwith, she wrote again: "Send me, I entreat you, Mrs. Halliday's address. I will go and see her. No, I can't do anything but work with my hands. I am no good for anything else. If Mrs. Halliday refuses me, I shall go as a servant into some other house. Don't mock at me; I don't deserve it. Write at once."

Till midnight she wept and prayed.

Geoffrey sent her the address, adding a few dry words: "If you are willing and able to carry out this project, your ambition ought to be satisfied. You will have done your part towards solving one of the gravest problems of the time." Rosamund did not at once understand; when the writer's meaning grew clear, she kept repeating the words, as though they were a new gospel. Yes! she would be working nobly, helping to show a way out of the great servant difficulty. It would be an example to poor ladies, like herself, who were ashamed of honest work. And Geoffrey Hunt was looking on. He must needs marvel; perhaps he would admire greatly; perhaps—oh, oh!

Of course, she found a difficulty in wording her letter to the lady who had never heard of her, and of whom she knew practically nothing. But zeal surmounted obstacles. She began by saying
that

that she was in search of domestic employment, and that, through her friends at Teddington, she had heard of Mrs. Halliday as a lady who might perhaps consider her application. Then followed an account of herself, tolerably ingenuous, and an amplification of the phrases she had addressed to Geoffrey Hunt. On an after-thought, she enclosed a stamped envelope.

Whilst the outcome remained dubious, Rosamund's behaviour to her fellow-boarders was a pattern of offensiveness. She no longer shunned them—seemed, indeed, to challenge their observation for the sake of meeting it with arrogant defiance. She rudely in-terrupted conversations, met sneers with virulent retorts, made herself the common enemy. Mrs. Banting was appealed to ; ladies declared that they could not live in a house where they were exposed to vulgar insult. When nearly a week had passed Mrs. Banting found it necessary to speak in private with Miss Jewell, and to make a plaintive remonstrance. Rosamund's flashing eye and contemptuous smile foretold the upshot.

"Spare yourself the trouble, Mrs. Banting. I leave the house to-morrow."

"Oh, but——"

"There is no need for another word. Of course, I shall pay the week in lieu of notice. I am busy, and have no time to waste."

The day before, she had been to Forest Hill, had seen Mrs. Halliday, and entered into an engagement. At midday on the morrow she arrived at the house which was henceforth to be her home, the scene of her labours.

Sheer stress of circumstance accounted for Mrs. Halliday's decision. Geoffrey Hunt, a dispassionate observer, was not misled in forming so high an opinion of his friend's wife. Only a year or two older than Rosamund, Mrs. Halliday had the mind and the

temper

temper which enable woman to front life as a rational combatant, instead of vegetating as a more or less destructive parasite. Her voice declared her ; it fell easily upon a soft, clear note ; the kind of voice that expresses good-humour and reasonableness, and many other admirable qualities ; womanly, but with no suggestion of the feminine gamut ; a voice that was never likely to test its compass in extremes. She had enjoyed a country breeding ; something of liberal education assisted her natural intelligence ; thanks to a good mother, she discharged with ability and content the prime domestic duties. But physically she was not inexhaustible, and the laborious, anxious years had taxed her health. A woman of the ignorant class may keep house, and bring up a family, with her own hands ; she has to deal only with the simplest demands of life ; her home is a shelter, her food is primitive, her children live or die according to the law of natural selection. Infinitely more complex, more trying, is the task of the educated wife and mother ; if to conscientiousness be added enduring poverty, it means not seldom an early death. Fatigue and self-denial had set upon Mrs. Halliday's features a stamp which could never be obliterated. Her husband, her children, suffered illnesses ; she, the indispensable, durst not confess even to a headache. Such servants as from time to time she had engaged merely increased her toil and anxieties ; she demanded, to be sure, the diligence and efficiency which in this new day can scarce be found among the menial ranks ; what she obtained was sluttish stupidity, grotesque presumption, and every form of female viciousness. Rosamund Jewell, honest in her extravagant fervour, seemed at first a mocking apparition ; only after a long talk, when Rosamund's ingenuousness had forcibly impressed her, would Mrs. Halliday agree to an experiment. Miss Jewell was to live as one of the family ; she did not ask this, but consented to it. She was to
receive

receive ten pounds a year, for Mrs. Halliday insisted that payment there must be.

"I can't cook," Rosamund had avowed. "I never boiled a potato in my life. If you teach me, I shall be grateful to you."

"The cooking I can do myself, and you can learn if you like."

"I should think I might wash and scrub by the light of nature?"

"Perhaps. Good will and ordinary muscles will go a long way."

"I can't sew, but I will learn."

Mrs. Halliday reflected.

"You know that you are exchanging freedom for a hard and a very dull life?"

"My life has been hard and dull enough, if you only knew. The work will seem hard at first, no doubt. But I don't think I shall be dull with you."

Mrs. Halliday held out her work-worn hand, and received a clasp of the fingers attenuated by idleness.

It was a poor little house; built—of course—with sham display of spaciousness in front, and huddling discomfort at the rear. Mrs. Halliday's servants never failed to urge the smallness of the rooms as an excuse for leaving them dirty; they had invariably been accustomed to lordly abodes, where their virtues could expand. The furniture was homely and no more than sufficient, but here and there on the walls shone a glimpse of summer landscape, done in better days by the master of the house, who knew something of various arts, but could not succeed in that of money-making. Rosamund bestowed her worldly goods in a tiny chamber which Mrs. Halliday did her best to make inviting and comfortable; she had less room here than at Mrs. Banting's, but the cleanliness of surroundings would depend upon herself, and she was not likely

to

to spend much time by the bedside in weary discontent. Halliday who came home each evening at half-past six, behaved to her on their first meeting with grave, even respectful, courtesy; his tone flattered Rosamund's ear, and nothing could have been more seemly than the modest gentleness of her replies.

At the close of the first day, she wrote to Geoffrey Hunt : " I do believe I have made a good beginning. Mrs. Halliday is perfect and I quite love her. Please do not answer this; I only write because I feel that I owe it to your kindness. I shall never be able to thank you enough."

When Geoffrey obeyed her and kept silence, she felt that he acted prudently; perhaps Mrs. Halliday might see the letter, and know his hand. But none the less she was disappointed.

Rosamund soon learnt the measure of her ignorance in domestic affairs. Thoroughly practical and systematic, her friend (this was to be their relation) set down a scheme of the day's and the week's work; it made a clear apportionment between them, with no preponderance of unpleasant drudgery for the new-comer's share. With astonishment, which she did not try to conceal, Rosamund awoke to the complexity and endlessness of home duties even in so small a house as this.

"Then you have *no* leisure ? " she exclaimed, in sympathy, not remonstrance.

"I feel at leisure when I'm sewing—and when I take the children out. And there's Sunday."

The eldest child was about five years old, the others three and a twelvemonth, respectively. Their ailments gave a good deal of trouble, and it often happened that Mrs. Halliday was awake with one of them the greater part of the night. For children Rosamund had no natural tenderness; to endure the constant sound of their voices proved, in the beginning, her hardest trial; but the

the resolve to school herself in every particular soon enabled her to tend the little ones with much patience, and insensibly she grew fond of them.   Until she had overcome her awkwardness in every task, it cost her no little effort to get through the day ; at bedtime she ached in every joint, and morning oppressed her with a sick lassitude.   Conscious however, of Mrs. Halliday's forbearance, she would not spare herself, and it soon surprised her to discover that the rigid performance of what seemed an ignoble task brought its reward.   Her first success in polishing a grate gave her more delight than she had known since childhood.   She summoned her friend to look, to admire, to praise.

"Haven't I done it well ?   Could you do it better yourself ? "

"Admirable ! "

Rosamund waved her black-lead brush and tasted victory.

The process of acclimatisation naturally affected her health. In a month's time she began to fear that she must break down ; she suffered painful disorders, crept out of sight to moan and shed a tear.   Always faint, she had no appetite for wholesome food. Tossing on her bed at night she said to herself a thousand times : "I must go on even if I die ! "   Her religion took the form of asceticism and bade her rejoice in her miseries ; she prayed constantly and at times knew the solace of an infinite self-glorification.   In such a mood she once said to Mrs. Halliday :

"Don't you think I deserve some praise for the step I took ? "

"You certainly deserve both praise and thanks from me."

"But I mean—it isn't every one who could have done it ?   I've a right to feel myself superior to the ordinary run of girls ? "

The other gave her an embarrassed look, and murmured a few satisfying words.   Later in the same day she talked to Rosamund about her health and insisted on making certain changes which allowed her to take more open-air exercise. The result of this

was

was a marked improvement ; at the end of the second month Rosamund began to feel and look better than she had done for several years. Work no longer exhausted her. And the labour in itself seemed to diminish, a natural consequence of perfect co-operation between the two women. Mrs. Halliday declared that life had never been so easy for her as now ; she knew the delight of rest in which there was no self-reproach. But for sufficient reasons she did not venture to express to Rosamund all the gratitude that was due.

About Christmas a letter from Forest Hill arrived at Teddington ; this time it did not forbid a reply. It spoke of struggles sufferings, achievements. " Do I not deserve a word of praise ? Have I not done something, as you said, towards solving the great question ? Don't you believe in me a little ? " Four more weeks went by, and brought no answer. Then, one evening, in a mood of bitterness, Rosamund took a singular step ; she wrote to Mr. Cheeseman. She had heard nothing of him, had utterly lost sight of the world in which they met ; but his place of business was known to her, and thither she addressed the note. A few lines only : " You are a very strange person, and I really take no interest whatever in you. But I have sometimes thought you would like to ask my forgiveness. If so, write to the above address—my sister's. I am living in London, and enjoying myself, but I don't choose to let you know where." Having an opportunity on the morrow, Sunday, she posted this in a remote district.

The next day, a letter arrived for her from Canada. Here was the explanation of Geoffrey's silence. His words could hardly have been more cordial, but there were so few of them. On nourishment such as this no illusion could support itself ; for the moment Rosamund renounced every hope. Well, she was no
worse

worse off than before the renewal of their friendship. But could it be called friendship? Geoffrey's mother and sisters paid no heed to her; they doubtless considered that she had finally sunk below their horizon; and Geoffrey himself, for all his fine words, most likely thought the same at heart. Of course they would never meet again. And for the rest of her life she would be nothing more than a domestic servant in genteel disguise— happy were the disguise preserved.

However, she had provided a distraction for her gloomy thoughts. With no more delay than was due to its transmission by way of Glasgow, there came a reply from Mr. Cheeseman: two sheets of notepaper. The writer prostrated himself; he had been guilty of shameful behaviour; even Miss Jewell, with all her sweet womanliness, must find it hard to think of him with charity. But let her remember what "the poets" had written about Remorse, and apply to *him* the most harrowing of their descriptions. He would be frank with her; he would "a plain, unvarnished tale unfold." Whilst away for his holiday he by chance encountered *one* with whom, in days gone by, he had held tender relations. She was a young widow; his foolish heart was touched; he sacrificed honour to the passing emotion. Their marriage would be delayed, for his affairs were just now any-thing but flourishing. "Dear Miss Jewell, will you not be my friend, my sister? Alas, I am not a happy man; but it is too late to lament." And so on to the squeezed signature at the bottom of the last page.

Rosamund allowed a fortnight to pass—not before writing, but before her letter was posted. She used a tone of condescension, mingled with airy banter. "From my heart I feel for you, but, as you say, there is no help. I am afraid you are very impulsive —yet I thought that was a fault of youth. Do not give way to despair.

despair. I really don't know whether I shall feel it right to let you hear again, but if it soothes you I don't think there would be any harm in your letting me know the cause of your troubles."

This odd correspondence, sometimes with intervals of three weeks, went on until late summer. Rosamund would soon have been a year with Mrs. Halliday. Her enthusiasm had long since burnt itself out; she was often a prey to vapours, to cheerless lassitude, even to the spirit of revolt against things in general, but on the whole she remained a thoroughly useful member of the household; the great experiment might fairly be called successful. At the end of August it was decided that the children must have sea air; their parents would take them away for a fortnight. When the project began to be talked of, Rosamund, perceiving a domestic difficulty, removed it by asking whether she would be at liberty to visit her sister in Scotland. Thus were things arranged.

Some days before that appointed for the general departure. Halliday received a letter which supplied him with a subject of conversation at breakfast.

"Hunt is going to be married," he remarked to his wife, just as Rosamund was bringing in the children's porridge.

Mrs. Halliday looked at her helper—for no more special reason than the fact of Rosamund's acquaintance with the Hunt family; she perceived a change of expression, an emotional play of feature, and at once averted her eyes.

"Where? In Canada? " she asked, off-hand.

"No, he's in England. But the lady is a Canadian.—I wonder he troubles to tell me. Hunt's a queer fellow. When we meet, once in two years, he treats me like a long-lost brother; but I don't think he'd care a bit if he never saw me or heard of me again."

"It's

"It's a family characteristic," interposed Rosamund with a dry laugh.

That day she moved about with the gait and the eyes of a somnambulist. She broke a piece of crockery, and became hysterical over it. Her afternoon leisure she spent in the bedroom, and at night she professed a headache which obliged her to retire early.

A passion of wrath inflamed her; as vehement—though so utterly unreasonable—as in the moment when she learnt the perfidy of Mr. Cheeseman. She raged at her folly in having submitted to social degradation on the mere hint of a man who uttered it in a spirit purely contemptuous. The whole hateful world had conspired against her. She banned her kinsfolk and all her acquaintances, especially the Hunts; she felt bitter even against the Hallidays—unsympathetic, selfish people, utterly indifferent to her private griefs, regarding her as a mere domestic machine. She would write to Geoffrey Hunt, and let him know very plainly what she thought of his behaviour in *urging* her to become a servant. Would such a thought have ever occurred to a *gentleman!* And her poor life was wasted, oh! oh! She would soon be thirty—thirty! The glass mocked her with savage truth. And she had not even a decent dress to put on. Self-neglect had made her appearance vulgar; her manners, her speech, doubtless, had lost their note of social superiority. Oh, it was hard! She wished for death, cried for divine justice in a better world.

On the morning of release, she travelled to London Bridge, ostensibly *en route* for the north. But, on alighting, she had her luggage taken to the cloak-room, and herself went by omnibus to the West-end. By noon she had engaged a lodging, one room in a street where she had never yet lived. And hither before night was transferred her property.

The

The next day she spent about half of her ready-money in the purchase of clothing—cheap, but such as the self-respect of a "lady" imperatively demands.   She bought cosmetics ; she set to work at removing from her hands the traces of ignoble occupation. On the day that followed—Sunday—early in the afternoon, she repaired to a certain corner of Kensington Gardens, where she came face to face with Mr. Cheeseman.

"I have come," said Rosamund, in a voice of nervous exhilaration which tried to subdue itself.   "Please to consider that it is more than you could expect."

"It is !   A thousand times more !   You are goodness itself."

In Rosamund's eyes the man had not improved since a year ago. The growth of a beard made him look older, and he seemed in indifferent health ; but his tremulous delight, his excessive homage, atoned for the defect.   She, on the other hand, was so greatly changed for the better that Cheeseman beheld her with no less wonder than admiration.   Her brisk step, her upright bearing, her clear eye, and pure-toned skin contrasted remarkably with the lassitude and sallowness he remembered ; at this moment, too, she had a pleasant rosiness of cheek which made her girlish, virginal. All was set off by the new drapery and millinery, which threw a shade upon Cheeseman's very respectable but somewhat time-honoured, Sunday costume.

They spent several hours together, Cheeseman talking of his faults, his virtues, his calamities, and his hopes, like the impulsive, well-meaning, but nerveless fellow that he was.   Rosamund gathered from it all, as she had vaguely learnt from his recent correspondence, that the alluring widow no longer claimed him ; but he did not enter into details on this delicate subject.   They had tea at a restaurant by Notting Hill Gate ; then, Miss Jewell appearing indefatigable, they again strolled in unfrequented ways.

At

At length was uttered the question for which Rosamund had long ago prepared her reply.

" You cannot expect me," she said sweetly, " to answer at once."

" Of course not ! I shouldn't have dared to hope——"

He choked and swallowed ; a few beads of perspiration shining on his troubled face.

" You have my address ; most likely I shall spend a week or two there. Of course you may write. I shall probably go to my sister's in Scotland, for the autumn——"

" Oh ! don't say that—don't. To lose you again—so soon——"

" I only said, ' probably '——"

" Oh, thank you !—To go so far away—And the autumn ; just when I have a little freedom ; the very best time—if I dared to hope such a thing——"

Rosamund graciously allowed him to bear her company as far as to the street in which she lived.

A few days later she wrote to Mrs. Halliday, heading her letter with the Glasgow address. She lamented the sudden impossibility of returning to her domestic duties. Something had happened. "In short, dear Mrs. Halliday, I am going to be married. I could not give you warning of this, it has come so unexpectedly. Do forgive me ! I so earnestly hope that you will find some one to take my place, some one better and more of a help to you. I know I haven't been much use. Do write home at Glasgow and say I may still regard you as a dear friend."

This having been dispatched, she sat musing over her prospects. Mr. Cheeseman had honestly confessed the smallness of his income ; he could barely count upon a hundred and fifty a year ; but things *might* improve. She did not dislike him—no, she did not dislike him. He would be a very tractable husband. Compared, of course, with——

A letter

A letter was brought up to her room. She knew the flowing commercial hand, and broke the envelope without emotion. Two sheets—three sheets—and a half. But what was all this ? "Despair . . . thoughts of self-destruction . . . ignoble publicity . . . practical ruin . . . impossible . . . despise and forget . . . Dante's hell . . . deeper than ever plummet sounded . . . forever ! . . . ." So again he had deceived her ! He must have known that the widow was dangerous ; his reticence was mere shuffling. His behaviour to that other woman had perhaps exceeded in baseness his treatment of herself ; else, how could he be so sure that a jury would give her " ruinous damages " ? Or was it all a mere illustration of a man's villainy ? Why should not *she* also sue for damages ? Why not ? Why not ?

The three months that followed were a time of graver peril, of darker crisis, than Rosamund, with all her slip-slop experiences, had ever known. An observer adequately supplied with facts, psychological and material, would more than once have felt that it depended on the mere toss of a coin whether she kept or lost her social respectability. She sounded all the depths possible to such a mind and heart—save only that from which there could have been no redemption. A saving memory lived within her, and at length, in the yellow gloom of a November morning—her tarnished, draggle-tailed finery thrown aside for the garb she had worn in lowliness—Rosamund betook herself to Forest Hill. The house of the Hallidays looked just as usual. She slunk up to the door, rang the bell, and waited in fear of a strange face. There appeared Mrs. Halliday herself. The surprised but friendly smile at once proved her forgiveness of Rosamund's desertion. She had written, indeed, with calm good sense, hoping only that all would be well.

" Let me see you alone, Mrs. Halliday.—How glad I am to sit in this room again ! Who is helping you now ? "

" No

" No one.   Help such as I want is not easy to find."

" Oh, let me come back !—I am *not* married.—No, no, there is nothing to be ashamed of.   I am no worse than I ever was.   I'll tell you everything—the whole silly, wretched story."

She told it, blurring only her existence of the past three months.

" I would have come before, but I was so bitterly ashamed.   I ran away so disgracefully.   Now I'm penniless—all but suffering hunger.   Will you have me again, Mrs. Halliday ?   I've been a horrid fool, but—I do believe—for the last time in my life.   Try me again, dear Mrs. Halliday ! "

There was no need of the miserable tears, the impassioned pleading.   Her home received her as though she had been absent but for an hour.   That night she knelt again by her bedside in the little room, and at seven o'clock next morning she was lighting fires, sweeping floors, mute in thankfulness.

Halliday heard the story from his wife, and shook a dreamy, compassionate head.

" For goodness' sake," urged the practical woman, " don't let her think she's a martyr."

" No, no ; but the poor girl should have her taste of happiness."

" Of course I'm sorry for her, but there are plenty of people more to be pitied.   Work she must, and there's only one kind of work she's fit for.   It's no small thing to find your vocation—is it ?   Thousands of such women—all meant by nature to scrub and cook—live and die miserably because they think themselves too good for it."

" The whole social structure is rotten ! "

" It'll last our time," rejoined Mrs. Halliday, as she gave a little laugh and stretched her weary arms.

George the Fourth

By Max Beerbohm

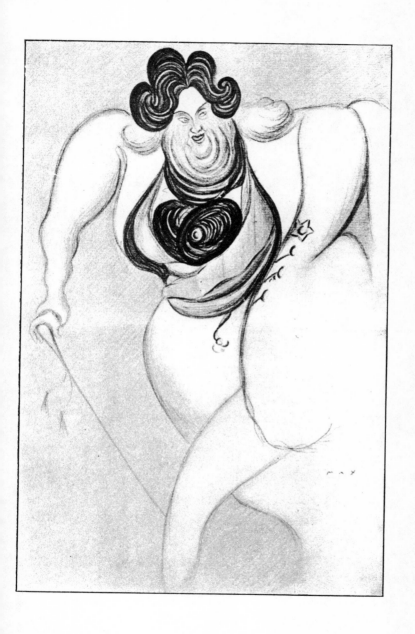

P'tit-Bleu

By Henry Harland

P'TIT-BLEU, poor P'tit-Bleu ! I can't name her without a sigh ; I can't think of her without a kind of heart-ache. Yet, all things considered, I wonder whether hers was really a destiny to sorrow over. True, she has disappeared ; and it is not pleasant to conjecture what she may have to come to, what may have befallen her, in the flesh, since her disappearance. But when I remember those beautiful preceding years of self-abnegation, of great love, and pain, and devotion, I find myself instinctively believing that something good she must have permanently gained ; some treasure that nothing, not the worst imaginable subsequent disaster, can quite have taken from her. It is not pleasant to conjecture what she may have done or suffered in the flesh ; but in the spirit, one may hope, she cannot have gone altogether to the bad, nor fared altogether ill.

In the spirit ! Dear me, there was a time when it would have seemed derisory to speak of the spirit in the same breath with P'tit-Bleu. In the early days of my acquaintance with her, for example, I should have stared if anybody had spoken of her spirit. If anybody had asked me to describe her, I should have said, " She is a captivating little animal, pretty and sprightly, but as soulless— as soulless as a squirrel." Oh, a warm-blooded little animal, good-
natured,

natured, quick-witted, full of life and the joy of life ; a delightful little animal to play with, to fondle ; but just a little animal, none the less : a little mass of soft, rosy, jocund, sensual, soulless matter. And in her full red lips, her roguish black eyes, her plump little hands, her trim, tight little figure—in her smile, her laugh—in the toss of her head—in her saucy, slightly swaggering carriage —I fancy you would have read my appreciation justified. No doubt there must have been the spark of a soul smouldering some-where in her (how, otherwise, account for what happened later on ?), but it was far too tiny a spark to be perceptible to the casual observer. Soul, however, I need hardly add, was the last thing we of the University were accustomed to look for in our feminine companions ; I must not for an instant seem to imply that the lack of a soul in P'tit-Bleu was a subject of mourning with any of us. That a Latin Quarter girl should be soulless was as much a part of the natural order of creation, as that she should be beardless. They were all of them little animals, and P'tit-Bleu diverged from the type principally in this, that where the others, in most instances, were stupid, objectionable little animals, she was a diverting one. She was made of sugar and spice and a hundred nice ingredients, whilst they were made of the dullest, vulgarest clay.

In my own case, P'tit-Bleu was the object, not indeed of love, but of a violent infatuation, at first sight.

At Bullier's, one evening, a chain of students, some twenty, linked hand in hand, were chasing her round and round the hall, shouting after her, in rough staccato, something that sounded like, " Ti-*bah !* Ti-*bah !* Ti-*bah !* "—while she, a sprite-like little form, in a black skirt and a scarlet bodice, fled before them with leaps and bounds, and laughed defiantly.

I hadn'

I hadn't the vaguest notion what " Ti-*bah !* Ti-*bah !* Ti-*bah !* "
meant, but that laughing face, with the red lips and the roguish
eyes, seemed to me immensely fascinating. Among the faces of
the other young ladies present—faces of dough, faces of tallow,
faces all weariness, staleness, and banality, common, coarse, point-
less, insipid faces—it shone like an epigram amongst platitudes, a
thing of fire amongst things of dust. I turned to some one near
me, and asked who she was.

" It's P'tit-Bleu, the dancing-girl. She's going to do a
quadrille."

P'tit-Bleu. . . . . It's the fashion, you know, in Paris, for the
girls who " do quadrilles " to adopt unlikely nicknames : aren't
the reigning favourites at this moment Chapeau-Mou and Fifi-la-
Galette ? P'tit-Bleu had derived hers from that vehement little
' wine of the barrier," which, the song declares, " vous met la
tête en feu." It was the tune of the same song, that, in another
minute, I heard the band strike up, in the balcony over our heads.
P'tit-Bleu came to a standstill in the middle of the floor, where
she was joined by three minor dancing-girls, to make two couples.
The chain of students closed in a circle round her. And the rest
of us thronged behind them, pressing forward, and craning our
necks. Then, as the band played, everybody sang, in noisy
chorus :

> " P'tit-Bleu, P'tit-Bleu, P'tit-Bleu-eu,
> Ça vous met la tête en feu !
> Ça vous ra-ra-ra-ra-ra,
> Ça vous ra-ra-ravigotte ! "

P'tit-Bleu stood with her hands on her hips, her arms a-kimbo,
her head thrown impudently back, her eyes sparkling mischievously,
her lips curling in a perpetual play of smiles, while her three
subalterns accomplished their tame preliminary measures ; and then
P'tit-Bleu

P'tit-Bleu pirouetted forward, and began her own indescribab
pas-seul—oh, indescribable for a hundred reasons. She wo
scarlet satin slippers, embroidered with black beads, and black si
stockings with scarlet clocks, and simply cataracts and cataracts
white diaphanous frills under her demure black skirt. And sh
danced with constantly increasing fervour, kicked higher an
higher, ever more boldly and more bravely. Presently her h
fell off, and she tossed it from her, calling to the member of th
crowd who had the luck to catch it, " Tiens mon chapeau ! " An
then her waving black hair flowed down her back, and flew loo
about her face and shoulders. And the whole time, she laughe
—laughed—laughed. With her swift whirlings, her astonishir
undulations, and the flashing of the red and black and white, one
eyes were dazzled. " Ça vous met la tête en feu ! " My hea
burned and reeled, as I watched her, and I thought, " What
delicious, bewitching little creature ! What wouldn't I give
know her ! " My head burned, and my heart yearned covetously
but I was a new-comer in the Quarter, and ignorant of its ea
etiquette, and terribly young and timid, and I should never hav
dared to speak to her without a proper introduction. She dance
with constantly increasing fervour, faster, faster, furiously fast : ti
suddenly—*zip !*—down she slid upon the floor, in the *grand écar*
and sat there (if one may call that posture sitting), smiling calm
up at us, whilst everybody thundered, " Bravo ! Bravo ! Bravo !

In an instant, though, she was on her feet again, and had darte
out of the circle to the side of the youth who had caught her ha
He offered it to her with a bow, but his pulses were thumpin
tempestuously, and no doubt she could read his envy in his eye
Anyhow, all at once, she put her arm through his, and said—o
thrills and wonders !—" Allons, mon petit, I authorise you
treat me to a bock."

It seemed as if impossible heavens had opened to me ; yet there she was, clinging to my arm, and drawing me towards the platform under the musicians' gallery, where there are tables for the thirsty. Her little plump white hand lay on my coat-sleeve ; the air was heady with the perfume of her garments ; her roguish black eyes were smiling encouragement into mine ; and her red lips were so near, so near, I had to fight down a wild impulse to stoop and snatch a kiss. She drew me towards the tables, and, on the way, she stopped before a mirror fixed on the wall and rearranged her hair ; while I stood close to her, still holding her hat, and waited, feeling the most exquisite proud swelling of the heart, as if I owned her. Her hair put right, she searched in her pocket and produced a small round ivory box, from which—having unscrewed its cover and handed it to me with a " Tiens ça "—she extracted a powder-puff ; and therewith she proceeded gently, daintily, to dust her face and throat, examining the effect critically in the glass the while. In the end she said, " Voilà, that's better," and turned her face to me for corroboration. " That's better, isn't it ? " " It's perfect. But—but you were perfect before, too," asseverated I. Oh, what a joy beyond measure thus to be singled out and made her confidant and adviser in these intimate affairs. . . . At our table, leaning back nonchalantly in her chair, as she quaffed her bock and puffed her cigarette, she looked like a bright-eyed, red-lipped bacchante.

I gazed at her in a quite unutterable ecstasy of admiration. My conscience told me that I ought to pay her a compliment upon her dancing ; but I couldn't shape one : my wits were paralysed by my emotions. I could only gaze, and gaze, and revel in my unexpected fortune. At last, however, the truth burst from me in a sort of involuntary gasp.

" But you are adorable—adorable."

She

She gave a quick smile of intelligence, of sympathy, and, with a knowing toss of the head and a provoking glance, suggested, " Je te mets la tête en feu, quoi ! "

She, you perceive, was entirely at her ease, mistress of the situation.   It is conceivable that she had met neophytes before—that I was by no means to her the unprecedented experience she was to me.   At any rate, she understood my agitation and sought to reassure me.

" Don't be afraid ; I'll not eat you," she promised.

I, in the depths of my mind, had been meditating what I could not but deem an excessively audacious proposal.   Her last speech gave me my cue, and I risked it.

" Perhaps you would like to eat something else ?   If—if we should go somewhere and sup ? "

" Monsieur thinks he will be safer to take precautions," she laughed.   " Well—I submit."

So we removed ourselves to the *vestiaire*, where she put on her cloak, and exchanged her slippers for a pair of boots (you can guess, perhaps, who enjoyed the beatific privilege of buttoning them for her) ; and then we left the Closerie des Lilas, falsely so called, with its flaring gas, its stifling atmosphere, its boisterous merrymakers, and walked arm in arm—only this time it was *my* arm that was within *hers*—down the Boul' Miche, past the Luxembourg gardens, where sweet airs blew in our faces, to the Gambrinus restaurant, in the Rue de Médicis.   And there you should have seen P'tit-Bleu devouring écrevisses.   Whatsoever this young woman's hand found to do, she did it with her might.   She attacked her écrevisses with the same jubilant abandon with which she had executed her bewildering single-step.   She devoured them with an energy, an enthusiasm, a thoroughness, that it was invigorating to witness ; smacking her lips, and smiling, and, from time to time,
                                                      between

between the mouthfuls, breathing soft little interjections of content. When the last pink shell was emptied, she threw herself back, and sighed, and explained, with delectable unconsciousness, " I was hungry." But at my venturing to protest, " Not really," she broke into mirthful laughter, and added, " At least, I had the appearance." Meanwhile, I must not fail to mention, she had done abundant honour to her share of a bottle of chablis. Don't be horrified—haven't the Germans, who ought to know, a proverb that recommends it ? " Wein auf Bier, das rath' ich Dir."

I have said that none of us mourned the absence of a soul in P'tit-Bleu. Nevertheless, as I looked at her to-night, and realised what a bright, joyous, good-humoured little thing she was, how healthy, and natural, and even, in a way, innocent she was, I suddenly felt a curious depression. She was all this, and yet . . . For just a moment, perhaps, I did vaguely mourn the lack of something. Oh, she was well enough for the present ; she was joyous, and good-humoured, and innocent in a way ; she was young and pretty, and the world smiled upon her. But—for the future ? When it occurred to me to think of her future—of what it must almost certainly be like, of what she must almost inevitably become —I confess my jaw dropped and the salt of our banquet lost its savour.

" What's the matter ? Why do you look at me like that ? " P'tit-Bleu demanded.

So I had to pull myself up and be jolly again. It was not altogether difficult. In the early twenties, troublesome reflections are easily banished, I believe ; and I had a lively comrade.

After her crayfish were disposed of, P'tit-Bleu called for coffee and lit a cigarette. And then, between whiffs and sips, she prattled gaily of the subject which, of all subjects, she was probably best qualified to treat, and which assuredly, for the time being,

possessed

possessed most interest for her listener—herself. She told me, as it were, the story of her birth, parentage, life, and exploits. It was the simplest story, the commonest story. Her mother (*la recherche de la paternité est interdite*), her mother had died when she was sixteen, and Jeanne (that was her baptismal name, Jeanne Mérois) had gone to work in the shop of a dressmaker, where, sewing hard from eight in the morning till seven at night, with an hour's intermission at noon, she could earn, in good seasons, as much as two-francs-fifty a day. Two and a half francs a day—say twelve shillings a week—in good seasons ; and one must eat, and lodge, and clothe one's body, and pay one's laundress, in good seasons and in bad. It scarcely satisfied her aspirations, and she took to dancing. Now she danced three nights a week at Bullier's, and during the day gave lessons in her art to a score of pupils, by which means she contrived to keep the wolf at a respectful distance from her door. "Tiens, here's my card," she concluded, and handed me an oblong bit of pasteboard, on which was printed, "P'tit-Bleu, Professeur de Danse, 22, Rue Monsieur le Prince."

"Et tu n'as pas d'amoureux ?" questioned I.

She flashed a look upon me that was quite inexpressibly arch, and responded instantly, with the charmingest little pout, "But yes—since I'm supping with him."

During the winter that followed, P'tit-Bleu and I supped together rather frequently. She was a mere little animal, she had no soul ; but she was the nicest little animal, and she had instincts. She was more than good-natured, she was kind-hearted ; and, according to her unconventional standards, she was conscientious. It would have amused and touched you, for example, if you had been taking her about, to notice her intense solicitude lest you should conduct her entertainment upon a scale too lavish, her

deprecating

deprecating frowns, her expostulations, her restraining hand laid on your arm. And the ordinary run of Latin Quarter girls derive an incommunicable rapture from seeing their cavaliers wantonly, purposelessly prodigal. With her own funds, on the contrary, P'tit-Bleu was free-handed to a fault : Mimi and Zizette knew whom to go to, when they were hard-up. Neither did she confine her benefactions to gifts of money, nor limit their operation to her particular sex. More than one impecunious student owed it to her skilful needle that his clothes were whole, and his linen maintained in a habitable state. " Fie, Chalks ! Your coat is torn, there are three buttons off your waistcoat, and your cuffs are frayed to a point that is disgraceful. I'll come round to-morrow afternoon, and mend them for you." And when poor Berthe Dumours was turned out of the hospital, in the dead of winter, half-cured, and without a penny in her purse, who took her in, and nursed her, and provided for her during her convalescence ?

Oh, she was a good little thing. " P'tit-Bleu's all right. There's nothing the matter with P'tit-Bleu," was Chalk's method of phrasing it.

At the same time, she could be trying, she could be exasperating. And she had a temper—a temper. What she made me suffer in the way of jealousy, during that winter, it would be gruesome to recount. She enjoyed an exceeding great popularity in the Quarter ; she was much run after. It were futile to pretend that she hadn't her caprices. And she held herself free as air. She would call no man master. You might take what she would give, and welcome ; but you must claim nothing as your due. You mustn't assume airs of proprietorship ; you mustn't presume upon the fact that she was supping with you to-night, to complain if she should sup to-morrow with another. Her concession of a privilege did not by any means imply that it was exclusive. She

would

would endure no exactions, no control or interference, no surveil-
lance, above all, no reproaches. Mercy, how angry she would
become if I ventured any, how hoighty-toighty and unap-
proachable.

"You imagine that I am your property ? Did you invent me ?
One would say you held a Government patent. All rights
reserved ! Thank you. You fancy perhaps that Paris is Con-
stantinople ? Ah, mais non ! "

She had a temper and a flow of language. There were
points you couldn't touch without precipitating hail and
lightning.

Thus my winter was far from a tranquil one, and before it
was half over I had three grey hairs. Honey and wormwood,
happiness and heartburn, reconciliations and frantic little tiffs,
carried us blithely on to Mi-Carême, when things reached a
crisis. . . . .

Mi-Carême fell midway in March that year : a velvety, sweet,
sunlit day, Spring stirring in her sleep. P'tit-Bleu and I had
spent the day together, in the crowded, crowded streets. We had
visited the Boulevards, of course, to watch the triumph of the
Queen of Washerwomen ; we had pelted everybody with confetti ;
and we had been pelted so profusely in return, that there were
confetti in our boots, in our pockets, down our necks, and
numberless confetti clung in the black meshes of P'tit-Bleu's hair,
like little pink, blue, and yellow stars. But all day long something
in P'tit-Bleu's manner, something in her voice, her smile, her
carriage, had obscurely troubled me ; something not easy to take
hold of, something elusive, unformulable, but disquieting. A
certain indefinite aloofness, perhaps ; an accentuated independence ;
as if she were preoccupied with secret thoughts, with intentions,
feelings, that she would not let me share.

And

And then, at night, we went to the Opera Ball.

P'tit-Bleu was dressed as an Odalisque : a tiny round Turkish cap, set jauntily sidewise on her head, a short Turkish jacket, both cap and jacket jingling and glittering with sequins ; a long veil of gauze, wreathed like a scarf round her shoulders ; then baggy Turkish trousers of blue silk, and scarlet Turkish slippers. Oh, she was worth seeing ; I was proud to have her on my arm. Her black crinkling hair, her dancing eyes, her eager face and red smiling mouth—the Sultan himself might have envied me such a houri. And many, in effect, were the envious glances that we encountered, as we made our way into the great brilliantly lighted ball-room, and moved hither and thither amongst the Harlequins and Columbines, the Pierrots, the Toréadors, the Shepherdesses and Vivandières, the countless fantastic masks, by whom the place was peopled. P'tit-Bleu had a *loup* of black velvet, which sometimes she wore, and sometimes gave to me to carry for her. I don't know when she looked the more dangerous, when she had it on, and her eyes glimmered mysteriously through its peep-holes, or when she had it off.

Many were the envious glances that we encountered, and presently I became aware that one individual was following us about : a horrid, glossy creature, in a dress suit, with a top-hat that was much too shiny, and a huge waxed moustache that he kept twirling invidiously : an undersized, dark, Hebraic-featured man, screamingly " rasta'." Whithersoever we turned, he hovered annoyingly near to us, and ogled P'tit-Bleu under my very beard. This was bad enough ; but—do sorrows ever come as single spies ?—conceive my emotions, if you please, when, by-and-by, suspicion hardened into certitude that P'tit-Bleu was not merely getting a vainglorious gratification from his attentions, but that she was positively playing up to them, encouraging him to persevere!

She

She chattered—to me, indeed, but at him—with a vivacity there was no misconstruing; laughed noisily, fluttered her fan, flirted her veil, donned and doffed her loup, and, I daresay, when my back was turned, exchanged actual eye-shots with the brute. . . . In due time quadrilles were organised, and P'tit-Bleu led a set. The glossy interloper was one of the admiring circle that surrounded her. Ugh! his complacent, insinuating smile, the conquering air with which he twirled his moustachios! And P'tit-Bleu. . . . When, at the finish, she sprang up, after her *grand écart*, what do you suppose she did ? . . . The brazen little minx, instead of rejoining *me*, slipped her arm through *his*, and went tripping off with him to the supper-room.

Oh, the night I passed, the night of anguish! The visions that tortured me, as I tramped my floor! The delirious revenges that I plotted, and gloated over in anticipation! She had left me —the mockery of it!—she had left me her loup, her little black velvet loup, with its empty eye-holes, and its horribly reminiscent smell. Everything P'tit-Bleu owned was scented with peau-d'Espagne. I wreaked my fury upon that loup, I promise you. I smote it with my palm, I ground it under my heel, I tore it limb from limb, I called it all manner of abusive names. Early in the morning I was at P'tit-Bleu's house; but the concierge grunted, "Pas rentrée." Oh, the coals thereof are coals of fire. I returned to her house a dozen times that day, and at length, towards night-fall, found her in. We had a stormy session, but of course, the last word of it was hers : still, for all slips, she was one of Eve's family. Of course she justified herself, and put me in the wrong. I went away, vowing I would never, never, never see her again. "Va! Ça m'est bien égal," she capped the climax by calling after me. Oh, youth! Oh, storm and stress! And to think that one lives to laugh at its memory.

For

For the rest of that season, P'tit-Bleu and I remained at daggers drawn. In June I left town for the summer; and then one thing and another happened, and kept me away till after Christmas.

When I got back, amongst the many pieces of news that I found waiting for me, there was one that affected P'tit-Bleu.

"P'tit-Bleu," I was told, "is 'collée' with an Englishman—but a grey-beard, mon cher—a gaga—an Englishman old enough to be her grandfather."

A stolid, implicit cynicism, I must warn you, was the mode of the Quarter. The student who did not wish to be contemned for a sentimentalist, dared never hesitate to believe an evil report, nor to put the worst possible construction upon all human actions. Therefore, when I was apprised by common rumour that during the dead season P'tit-Bleu (for considerations fiscal, *bien entendu*) had gone to live " collée " with an Englishman old enough to be her grandfather—though, as it turned out, the story was the sheerest fabrication—it never entered my head to doubt it.

At the same time, I confess, I could not quite share the humour of my compeers, who regarded the circumstance as a stupendous joke. On the contrary, I was shocked and sickened. I shouldn't have imagined her capable of that. She was a mere little animal; she had no soul; she was bound, in the nature of things, to go from bad to worse, as I had permitted myself, indeed, to admonish her, in the last conversation we had had. "Mark my words, you will go from bad to worse." But I had thought her such a nice little animal; in my secret heart, I had hoped that her progress would be slow—even, faintly, that Providence might let something happen to arrest it, to divert it. And now. . . . !

As a matter of fact, Providence *had* let something happen to divert it; and that something was this very relation of hers with

an

an old Englishman, in which the scandal-lovers of the Latin Quarter were determined to see neither more nor less than a mercenary "collage." The diversion in question, however, was an extremely gradual process. As yet, it is pretty certain, P'tit-Bleu herself had never so much as dreamed that any diversion was impending.

But she knew that her relation with the Englishman was an innocent relation ; and of its innocence, I am glad to be able to record, she succeeded in convincing one, at least, of her friends, tolerably early in the game. In the teeth of my opposition, and at the expense of her own pride, she forced an explanation, which, I am glad to say, convinced me.

I had just passed her and her Englishman in the street. They were crossing the Boulevard St. Michel, and she was hanging on his arm, looking up into his face, and laughing. She wore a broad-brimmed black hat, with a red ribbon in it, and a knot of red ribbon at her throat ; there was a lovely suggestion of the same colour in her cheeks ; and never had her eyes gleamed with sincerer fun.

I assure you, the sensation this spectacle afforded me amounted to a physical pain—the disgust, the anger. If she could laugh like that, how little could she feel her position ! The hardened shamelessness of it !

Turning from her to her companion, I own I was surprised and puzzled. He was a tall, spare old man, not a grey-beard, but a white-beard, and he had thin snow-white hair. He was dressed neatly indeed, but the very reverse of sumptuously. His black overcoat was threadbare, his carefully polished boots were patched. Yet, everybody averred, it was his affluence that had attracted her ; she had taken up with him during the dead season, because she had been "à sec." A detail that did nothing to relieve my perplexit perplexity was the character of his face. Instead of the florid concupiscent face, with coarse lips and fiery eye-balls, I had instinctively expected, I saw a thin, pale face, with mild, melancholy eyes, a gentle face, a refined face, rather a weak face, certainly the very last face the situation called for. He *was* a beast of course, but he didn't look like a beast. He looked like a gentleman, a broken-down, forlorn old gentleman, singularly astray from his proper orbit.

They were crossing the Boulevard St. Michel as I was leaving the Café Vachette ; and at the corner of the Rue des Ecoles we came front to front. P'tit-Bleu glanced up ; her eyes brightened, she gave a little start, and was plainly for stopping to shake hands. I cut her dead. . . .

I cut her dead, and held my course serenely down the Boulevard —though I'm not sure my heart wasn't pounding. But I could lay as unction to my soul the consciousness of having done the appropriate thing, of having marked my righteous indignation.

In a minute, however, I heard the pat-pat of rapid footsteps on the pavement behind me, and my name being called. I hurried on, careful not to turn my head. But, at Cluny, P'tit-Bleu arrived abreast of me.

" I want to speak to you," she gasped, out of breath from running.

I shrugged my shoulders.

" Will you tell me why you cut me like that just now ? "

" If you don't know, I doubt if I could make you understand," I answered, with an air of imperial disdain.

" You bear me a grudge, hein ? For what I did last March ? Well, then, you are right. There. I was abominable. But I have been sorry, and I ask your pardon. Now will you let bygones be bygones ? Will you forgive me ? "

                                                    " Oh,"

"Oh," I said, "don't try to play the simpleton with me. You are perfectly well aware that isn't why I cut you."

"But why, then ? " cried she, admirably counterfeiting (as I took for granted) a look and accent of bewilderment.

I walked on without speaking. She kept beside me.

"But why, then ? If it isn't that, what is it ? "

"Oh, bah ! "

"I insist upon your telling me. Tell me."

"Very good, then. I don't care to know a girl who lives 'collée' with a gaga," I said, brutally.

P'tit-Bleu flushed suddenly, and faced me with blazing eyes.

"Comment ! You believe that ? " she cried.

"Pooh ! " said I.

"Oh, mais non, mais non, mais non, alors ! You don't believe that ? "

"You pay me a poor compliment. Why should you expect me to be ignorant of a thing the whole Quarter knows ? "

"Oh, the whole Quarter ! What does that matter to me, your Quarter ? Those nasty little students ! C'est de la crasse, quoi ! They may believe—they may say—-what they like. Oh, ça m'est bien égal ! " with a shake of the head and a skyward gesture. " But you—but my friends ! Am I that sort of girl ? Answer."

"There's only one sort of girl in the precincts of this University," declared her disenchanted interlocutor. "You're all of one pattern. The man's an ass who expects any good from any of you. Don't pose as better than the others. You're all a—un tas de saletés. I'm sick and tired of the whole sordid, squalid lot of you. I should be greatly obliged, now, if you would have the kindness to leave me. Go back to your gaga. He'll be impatient waiting."

That speech, I fancied, would rid me of her. But no.

"You

"You are trying to make me angry, aren't you? But I refuse to leave you till you have admitted that you are wrong," she persisted. "It's an outrageous slander. Monsieur Long (that is his name, Monsieur Long), he lives in the same house with me, on the same landing; et voilà tout. Dame! Can I prevent him? Am I the landlord? And, for that, they say I'm 'collée' with him. I don't care what they say. But you! I swear to you it is an infamous lie. Will you come home with me now, and see?"

"Oh, that's mere quibbling. You go with him everywhere, you dine with him, you are never seen without him."

"Dieu de Dieu!" wailed P'tit-Bleu. "How shall I convince you? He is my neighbour. Is it forbidden to know one's neighbours? I swear to you, I give you my word of honour, it is nothing else. How to make you believe me?"

"Well, my dear," said I, "if you wish me to believe you, break with him. Chuck him up. Drop his acquaintance. Nobody in his senses will believe you so long as you go trapesing about the Quarter with him."

"Oh, but no," she cried, "I can't drop his acquaintance."

"Ah, there it is," cried I.

"There are reasons. There are reasons why I can't, why I mustn't."

"I thought so."

"Ah, voyons!" she broke out, losing patience. "Will you not believe my word of honour? Will you force me to tell you things that don't concern you—that I have no right to tell? Well, then, listen. I cannot drop his acquaintance, because—this is a secret—he would die of shame if he thought I had betrayed it —you will never breathe it to a soul—because I have discovered that he has a—a vice, a weakness. No—but listen. He is an
Englishman,

Englishman, a painter. Oh, a painter of great talent ; a painter
who has exposed at the Salon—quoi ! A painter who is known
in his country. On a même parlé de lui dans les journaux ;
voilà. But look. He has a vice. He has half ruined, half
killed himself with a drug. Yes—opium. Oh, but wait, wait.
I will tell you. He came to live in our house last July, in the
room opposite mine. When we met, on the landing, in the
staircase, he took off his hat, and we passed the bonjour. Oh, he
is a gentleman ; he has been well brought up. From that we
arrived at speaking together a little, and then at visiting. It was
the dead season, I had no affairs. I would sit in his room in the
afternoon, and we would chat. Oh, he is a fine talker. But,
though he had canvases, colours, all that is needed for painting,
he never painted. He would only talk, talk. I said, ' But you
ought to paint.' He said always, ' Yes, I must begin something
to-morrow.' Always to-morrow. And then I discovered what
it was. He took opium. He spent all his money for opium.
And when he had taken his opium he would not work, he
would only talk, talk, talk, and then sleep, sleep. You think
that is well—hein ? That a painter of talent should do no
work, but spend all his money for a drug, for a poison, and
then say ' To-morrow ' ? You think I could sit still and see
him commit these follies under my eyes and say nothing, do nothing ? Ruin his brain, his health, his career, and waste all his
money, for that drug ? Oh, mais non. I made him the sermon.
I said, ' You know it is very bad, that which you are doing
there.' I scolded him. I said, ' But I forbid you to do that—do
you understand ? I forbid it.' I went with him everywhere, I
gave him all my time ; and when he would take his drug I would
annoy him, I would make a scene, I would shame him. Well,
in the end, I have acquired an influence over him. He has submitted

mitted himself to me. He is really trying to break the habit. I keep all his money. I give him his doses. I regulate them, I diminish them. The consequence is, I make him work. I give him one very small dose in the morning to begin the day. Then I will give him no more till he has done so much work. You see ? Tu te figures que je suis sa maîtresse ? Je suis plutôt sa nounou—va ! Je suis sa caissière. And he is painting a great picture—you will see. Eh bien, how can I give up his acquaintance ? Can I let him relapse, as he would do to-morrow without me, into his bad habit ? "

I was walking with long strides, P'tit-Bleu tripping at my elbow ; and before her story was finished we had left the Boulevard behind us, and reached the middle of the Pont St. Michel. There, I don't know why, we halted, and stood looking off towards Notre-Dame. The grim grey front of the Cathedral glowed softly amethystine in the afternoon sun, and the sky was infinitely deep and blue above it. One could be intensely conscious of the splendid penetrating beauty of this picture, without, somehow, giving the less attention to what P'tit-Bleu was saying. She talked swiftly, eagerly, with constantly changing, persuasive intonations, with little brief pauses, hesitations, with many gestures, with much play of eyes and face. When she had done, I waited a moment. Then, grudgingly, "Well," I began, "if what you tell me is true——"

" *If* it is true ! " P'tit-Bleu cried, with sudden fierceness. " Do you dare to say you doubt it ? "

And she gazed intently, fiercely, into my eyes, challenging me, as it were, to give her the lie.

Before that gaze my eyes dropped, abashed.

" No—I don't doubt it," I faltered, " I believe you. And—and allow me to say that you are a—a damned decent little girl."

Poor

Poor P'tit-Bleu! How shall I tell you the rest of her story —the story of those long years of love and sacrifice and devotion, and of continual discouragement, disappointment, with his death at the end of them, and her disappearance ?

In the beginning she herself was very far from realising what she had undertaken, what had befallen her. To exercise a little friendly supervision over her neighbour's addiction to opium, to husband his money for him, and spur him on to work—it seemed a mere incident in her life, an affair by the way. But it became her exclusive occupation, her whole life's chief concern. Little by little, one after the other, she put aside all her former interests, thoughts, associations, dropped all her former engagements, to give herself as completely to caring for, guarding, guiding poor old Edward Long, as if she had been a mother, and he her helpless child.

Throughout that first winter, indeed, she continued to dance at Bullier's, continued to instruct her corps of pupils, and continued even occasionally, though much less frequently than of old time, to be seen at the Vachette, or to sup with a friend at the Gambrinus. But from day to day Monsieur Edouard (he had soon ceased to be Monsieur Long, and become Monsieur Edouard) absorbed more and more of her time and attention ; and when the spring came she suddenly burned her ships.

You must understand that she had one pertinacious adversary in her efforts to wean him of his vice. Not an avowed adversary, for he professed the most earnest wish that she might be successful ; but an adversary who was eternally putting spokes in her wheel, all the same. Yes, Monsieur Edouard himself. Never content with the short rations to which she had condemned him, he was perpetually on the watch for a chance to elude her vigilance ; she was perpetually discovering that he had somehow contrived

trived to lay in secret supplies.   And every now and again, openly
defying her authority, he would go off for a grand debauch.
Then her task of reducing his daily portion to a minimum must
needs be begun anew.   Well, when the spring came, and the
Salon opened, where his picture (*her* picture ?) had been received
and very fairly hung, they went together to the Vernissage.
And there he met a whole flock of English folk—artists and
critics, who had " just run over for the show, you know "—with
whom he was acquainted ; and they insisted on carrying him away
with them to lunch at the Ambassadeurs.

I, too, had assisted at the Vernissage ; and when I left it, I
found P'tit-Bleu seated alone under the trees in the Champs-
Elysées.   She had on a brilliant spring toilette, with a hat and a
sunshade. . . . Oh, my dear ! It is not to be denied that P'tit-
Bleu had the courage of her tastes.   But her face was pale, and
her lips were drawn down, and her eyes looked strained and
anxious.

" What's the row ? " I asked.

And she told me how she had been abandoned—" plantée là "
was her expression—and of course I invited her to lunch with me.
But she scarce relished the repast.   " Pourvu qu'il ne fasse pas de
bêtises ! " was her refrain.

She returned rather early to the Rue Monsieur le Prince, to see
if he had come home ; but he hadn't.   Nor did he come home
that night, nor the next day, nor the next.   At the week's end,
though, he came : dirty, haggard, tremulous, with red eyes, and
nude—yes, nude—of everything save his shirt and trousers ! He
had borrowed a sovereign from one of his London friends, and
when that was gone, he had pledged or sold everything but his
shirt and trousers—hat, boots, coat, everything.   It was an equally
haggard and red-eyed P'tit-Bleu who faced him on his reappearance.

ance. And I've no doubt she gave him a specimen of her eloquence. "You figure to yourself that this sort of thing amuses me, hein ? Here are six good days and nights that I haven't been able to sleep or rest."

Explaining the case to me, she said, "Ah, what I suffered ! I could never have believed that I cared so much for him. But—what would you ?—one attaches oneself, you know. Ah, what I suffered ! The anxiety, the terrors ! I expected to hear of him run over in the streets. Well, now, I must make an end of this business. I'm going to take him away. So long as he remains in Paris, where there are chemists who will sell him that filthiness (cette crasse) it is hopeless. No sooner do I get my house of cards nicely built up, than—piff !—something happens to knock it over. I am going to take him down into the country, far from any town, far from the railway, where I can guard him better. I know a place, a farm-house, near Villiers-St.-Jacques, where we can get board. He has a little income, which reaches him every three months from England. Oh, very little, but if I am careful of it, it will pay our way. And then—I will make him work."

"Oh, no," I protested. "You're not going to leave the Quarter." And I'm ashamed to acknowledge, I laboured hard to dissuade her. "Think of how we'll miss you. Think of how you'll bore yourself. And anyhow, he's not worth it. And besides, you won't succeed. A man who has an appetite for opium will get it, coûte que coûte. He'd walk twenty miles in bare feet to get it." This was the argument that I repeated in a dozen different paraphrases. You see, I hadn't realised yet that it didn't matter an atom whether she succeeded, or whether he was worth it. He was a mere instrument in the hands of Providence. Let her succeed or let her fail in keeping him from opium : the important

important thing . . . how shall I put it ? This little Undine had risen out of the black waters of the Latin Quarter and attached herself to a mortal. What is it that love gains for Undines ?

"Que veux-tu ? " cried P'tit-Bleu. " I am fond of him. I can't bear to see him ruining himself. I must do what I can."

And the Quarter said, " Ho-ho ! You chaps who didn't believe it was a ' collage ' ! He-he ! What do you say now ? She's chucked up everything, to go and live in the country with him."

In August or September I ran down to the farm-house near Villiers-St.-Jacques, and passed a week with them. I found a mightily changed Monsieur Edouard, and a curiously changed P'tit-Bleu, as well. He was fat and rosy, he who had been so thin and white. And she—she was *grave.* Yes, P'tit-Bleu was grave : sober, staid, serious. And her impish, mocking black eyes shone with a strange, serious, calm light.

Monsieur Edouard (with whom my relations had long before this become confidential) drew me apart, and told me he was having an exceedingly bad time of it.

" She's really too absurd, you know. She's a martinet, a tyrant. Opium is to me what tobacco is to you, and does me no more harm. I need it for my work. Oh, in moderation ; of course one can be excessive. Yet she refuses to let me have a tenth of my proper quantity. And besides, how utterly senseless it is, keeping me down here in the country. I'm dying of ennui. There's not a person I can have any sort of intellectual sympathy with, for miles in every direction. An artist needs the stimulus of contact with his fellows. It's indispensable. If she'd only let me run up

to

to Paris for a day or two at a time, once a month say. Couldn't
you persuade her to let me go back with you ? She's the most
awful screw, you know. It's the French lower middle class
parsimony. I'm never allowed to have twopence in my pocket.
Yet whose money is it ? Where does it come from ? I really
can't think why I submit, why I don't break away from her, and
follow my own wishes. But the poor little thing is fond of me ;
she's attached herself to me. I don't know what would become of
her if I cast her off. Oh, don't fancy that I don't appreciate
her. Her intentions are excellent. But she lacks wisdom, and
she enjoys the exercise of power. I wish you'd speak with
her."

P'tit-Bleu also drew me apart.

"Please don't call me P'tit-Bleu any more. Call me Jeanne.
I have put all that behind me—all that P'tit-Bleu signifies. I
hate to think of it, to be reminded of it. I should like to
forget it."

When I had promised not to call her P'tit-Bleu any more, she
went on, replying to my questions, to tell me of their life.

"Of course, everybody thinks I am his mistress. You can't
convince them I'm not. But that's got to be endured. For the
rest, all is going well. You see how he is improved. I give him
fifteen drops of laudanum, morning, noon, and night. Fifteen
drops—it is nothing. I could take it myself, and never know it.
And he used to drink off an ounce—an ounce, mon cher—at a
time, and then want more at the end of an hour. Yes ! Oh,
he complains, he complains of everything, he frets, he is not
contented. But he has not walked twenty miles in bare feet,
as you said he would. And he is working. You will see his
pictures."

"And you—how do you pass your time ? What do you do ? "

"I pose

"I pose for him a good deal. And then I have much sewing to do. I take in sewing for Madame Deschamps, the deputy's wife, to help to make the ends meet. And then I read. Madame Deschamps lends me books."

"And I suppose you're bored to death?"

"Oh, no, I am not bored. I am happy. I never was really happy—dans le temps."

They were living in a very plain way indeed. You know what French farmhouses are apt to be. His whole income was under a hundred pounds a year ; and out of that (and the trifle she earned by needlework) his canvases, colours, brushes, frames, had to be paid for, as well as his opium, and their food, clothing, everything. But P'tit-Bleu—Jeanne—with that "lower-middle-class parsimony" of hers, managed somehow. Jeanne ! In putting off the name, she had put off also, in great measure, the attributes of P'tit-Bleu ; she had become Jeanne in nature. She was grave, she was quiet. She wore the severest black frocks—she made them herself. And I never once noticed the odour of peau-d'Espagne, from the beginning to the end of my visit. But—shall I own it ? Jeanne was certainly the more estimable of the two women, but shall I own that I found her far less exciting as a comrade than P'tit-Bleu had been ? She was good, but she wasn't very lively or very amusing.

P'tit-Bleu, the heroine of Bullier's, that lover of noisy pleasure, of daring toilettes, of risky perfumes, of écrevisses and chablis, of all the rush and dissipation of the Boul' Miche and the Luxembourg, quietly settling down into Jeanne of the home-made frocks, in a rough French farmhouse, to a diet of veal and lentils, lentils and veal, seven times a week, and no other pastime in life than the devoted, untiring nursing of an ungrateful old English opium-eater—here was variation under domestication with a vengeance.

And

And on Sunday . . . P'tit-Bleu went twice to church !

About ten days after my return to Paris, there came a rat-ta-ta-tat at my door, and P'tit-Bleu walked in—pale, with wide eyes. " I don't know how he has contrived it, but he must have got some money somewhere, and walked to the railway, and come to town. Anyhow, here are three days that he has disappeared. What to do ? What to do ? " She was in a deplorable state of mind, poor thing, and I scarcely knew how to help her. I proposed that we should take counsel with a Commissary of Police. But when that functionary discovered that she was neither the wife nor daughter of the missing man, he smiled, and remarked, " It is not our business to recover ladies' protectors for them." P'tit-Bleu walked the streets in quest of him, all day long and very nearly all night long too, for close upon a fortnight. In the end, she met him on the quays—dazed, half-imbecile, and again nude of everything save his shirt and trousers. So, again, having nicely built up her house of cards—piff !—something had happened to topple it over.

" Let him go to the devil his own way," said I. " Really, he's unworthy of your pains."

" No, I can't leave him. You see, I'm fond of him," said she.

He, however, positively refused to return to the country. " The fact is," he explained, " I ought to go to London. Yes, it will be well for me to pass the winter in London. I should like to have a show there, a one-man show, you know. I dare say I could sell a good many pictures, and get orders for portraits." So they went to London. In the spring I received a letter from P'tit-Bleu—a letter full of orthographic faults, if you like—but a letter that I treasure. Here's a translation of it :

" My

"My dear Friend,

"I have hesitated much before taking my pen in hand to write to you. But I have no one else to turn to. We have had a dreadful winter. Owing to my ignorance of the language one speaks in this dirty town, I have not been able to exercise over Monsieur Edouard that supervision of which he has need. In consequence, he has given himself up to the evil habit which you know, as never before. Every penny, every last sou, which he could command, has been spent for that detestable filth. Many times we have passed whole days without eating, no, not the end of a crust. He has no desire to eat when he has had his dose. We are living in a slum of the most disgusting, in the quarter of London they call Soho. Everything we have, save the bare necessary of covering, has been put with the lender-on-pledges. Yesterday I found a piece of one shilling in the street. That, however, I have been forced to dispense for opium, because, when he has had such large quantities, he would die or go mad if suddenly deprived.

"I have addressed myself to his family, but without effect. They refuse to recognise me. Everybody here, of course, figures to himself that I am his mistress. He has two brothers, on of the army, one an advocate. I have besieged them in vain. They say, 'We have done for him all that is possible. We can do no more. He has exhausted our patience. Now that he has gone a step farther, and, in his age, disgraced himself by living with a mistress, as well as besotting himself with opium, we wash our hands of him for good.' And yet, I cannot leave him, because I know, without me, he would kill himself within the month, by his excesses. To his sisters, both of whom are married and ladies of the world, I have appealed with equal results. They refuse to regard me otherwise than as his mistress.

"But I cannot bear to see that great man, with that mind, that talent, doing himself to death. And when he is not under the influence of his drug, who is so great? Who has the wit, the wisdom, the heart, the charm, of Monsieur Edouard? Who can paint like him?

"My

"My dear, as a last resource, I take up my pen to ask you for assistance. If you could see him your heart would be moved. He is so thin, so thin, and his face has become *blue*, yes, blue, like the face of a dead man. Help me to save him from himself. If you can send me a note of five hundred francs, I can pay off our indebtedness here, and bring him back to France, where, in a sane country, far from a town, again I can reduce him to a few drops of laudanum a day, and again see him in health and at work. That which it costs me to make this request of you, I have not the words to tell you. But, at the end of my forces, having no other means, no other support, I confide myself to your well-tried amity.

"I give you a good kiss.

"JEANNE."

If the reading of this letter brought a lump into my throat and something like tears into my eyes—if I hastened to a banker's, and sent P'tit-Bleu the money she asked for, by telegraph—if I reproached her bitterly and sincerely for not having applied to me long before,—I hope you will believe that it wasn't for the sake of Monsieur Edouard.

They established themselves at St.-Etienne, a hamlet on the coast of Normandy, to be further from Paris. Dieppe was their nearest town. They lived at St.-Etienne for nearly three years. But, periodically, when she had got her house of cards nicely built up—piff!—he would walk into Dieppe.

He walked into Dieppe one day in the autumn of 1885, and it took her a week to find him. He was always ill, after one of his grand debauches. This time he was worse than he had ever been before. I can imagine the care with which she nursed him, her anxious watching by his bedside, her prayers, her hope, the blankness when he died.

She came back to Paris, and called three times at my lodgings.
But

But I was in England, and didn't receive the notes she left till nearly six months afterwards. I have never seen her since, never heard from her.

What has become of her ? It is not pleasant to conjecture. Of course, after his death, she ought to have died too. But the Angel of this Life,

> "Whose care is lest men see too much at once,"

couldn't permit any such satisfying termination. So she has simply disappeared, and, in the flesh, may have come to . . . one would rather not conjecture. All the same, I can't believe that in the spirit she will have made utter shipwreck. I can't believe that nothing permanent was won by those long years of love and pain. Her house of cards was toppled over, as often as she built it up ; but perhaps she was all the while building another house, a house not made with hands, a house, a temple, indestructible.

Poor P'tit Bleu !

Rustem Firing the First Shot

By Patten Wilson

A Letter Home

By Enoch Arnold Bennett

I

RAIN was falling—it had fallen steadily through the night—but the sky showed promise of fairer weather. As the first streaks of dawn appeared, the wind died away, and the young leaves on the trees were almost silent. The birds were insistently clamorous, vociferating times without number that it was a healthy spring morning and good to be alive.

A little, bedraggled crowd stood before the park gates, awaiting the hour named on the notice board when they would be admitted to such lodging and shelter as iron seats and overspreading branches might afford. A weary patient-eyed, dogged crowd—a dozen men, a boy of thirteen, and a couple of women, both past middle age—which had been gathering slowly since five o'clock. The boy appeared to be the least uncomfortable. His feet were bare, but he had slept well in an area in Grosvenor Place, and was not very damp yet. The women had nodded on many doorsteps, and were soaked. They stood apart from the men, who seemed unconscious of their existence. The men were exactly such as one would have expected to find there—beery and restless as to the eyes, quaintly shod, and with nondescript greenish clothes which

for

for the most part bore traces of the yoke of the sandwich board. Only one amongst them was different.

He was young, and his cap, and manner of wearing it, gave sign of the sea. His face showed the rough outlines of his history. Yet it was a transparently honest face, very pale, but still boyish and fresh enough to make one wonder by what rapid descent he had reached his present level. Perhaps the receding chin, the heavy, pouting lower lip, and the ceaselessly twitching mouth offered a key to the problem.

"Say, Darkey," he said.

"Well ? "

"How much longer ? "

"Can't ye see the clock ? It's staring ye in the face."

"No. Something queer's come over my eyes."

Darkey was a short, sturdy man, who kept his head down and his hands deep in his pockets. The rain-drops clinging to the rim of an ancient hat fell every now and then into his grey beard, which presented a drowned appearance. He was a person of long and varied experiences ; he knew that queer feeling in the eyes, and his heart softened.

"Come, lean against the pillar," he said, "if you don't want to tumble. Three of brandy's what you want. There's four minutes to wait yet."

With body flattened to the masonry, legs apart, and head thrown back, Darkey's companion felt more secure, and his mercurial spirits began to revive. He took off his cap, and brushing back his light brown curly hair with the hand which held it, he looked down at Darkey through half-closed eyes, the play of his features divided between a smile and a yawn. He had a lively sense of humour, and the irony of his situation was not lost on him. He took a grim, ferocious delight in calling up the might-have-beens night-have-beens and the "fatuous ineffectual yesterdays" of life. There is a certain sardonic satisfaction to be gleaned from a frank recognition of the fact that you are the architect of your own misfortune. He felt that satisfaction, and laughed at Darkey, who was one of those who bleat about "ill-luck" and "victims of circumstance."

"No doubt," he would say, "you're a very deserving fellow, Darkey, who's been treated badly. I'm not." To have attained such wisdom at twenty-five is not to have lived altogether in vain.

A park-keeper presently arrived to unlock the gates, and the band of outcasts straggled indolently towards the nearest sheltered seats. Some went to sleep at once, in a sitting posture. Darkey produced a clay pipe, and, charging it with a few shreds of tobacco laboriously gathered from his waistcoat pocket, began to smoke. He was accustomed to this sort of thing, and with a pipe in his mouth could contrive to be moderately philosophical upon occasion. He looked curiously at his companion, who lay stretched at full length on another bench.

"I say, pal," he remarked, "I've known ye two days; ye've never told me yer name, and I don't ask ye to. But I see ye've got slep' in a park before."

"You hit it, Darkey; but how?"

"Well, if the keeper catches ye lying down he'll be on to ye. Lying down's not allowed."

The man raised himself on his elbow.

"Really now," he said, "that's interesting. But I think I'll give the keeper the opportunity of moving me. Why, it's quite fine, the sun's coming out and the sparrows are hopping round—cheeky little devils! I'm not sure that I don't feel jolly."

"I wish I'd got the price of a pint about me," sighed Darkey,
and

and the other man dropped his head and appeared to sleep. Then Darkey dozed a little and heard in his waking sleep the heavy, crunching tread of an approaching park-keeper; he started up to warn his companion, but thought better of it, and closed his eyes again.

"Now then, there," the park-keeper shouted to the man with the sailor hat, "get up! This ain't a fourpenny doss, you know. No lying down." A rough shake accompanied the words, and the man sat up.

"All right, my friend." The keeper, who was a good-humoured man, passed on without further objurgation.

The face of the younger man had grown whiter.

"Look here, Darkey," he said, "I believe I'm done for."

"Never say die."

"No, just die without speaking." His head fell forward and his eyes closed.

"At any rate, this is better than some deaths I've seen," he began again with a strange accession of liveliness. "Darkey, did I tell you the story of the five Japanese girls?"

"What, in Suez Bay?" said Darkey, who had heard many sea stories during the last two days, and recollected them but hazily.

"No, man. This was at Nagasaki. We were taking in a cargo of coal for Hong Kong. Hundreds of little Jap girls pass the coal from hand to hand over the ship's side in tiny baskets that hold about a plateful. In that way you can get 3000 tons aboard in two days."

"Talking of platefuls reminds me of sausage and mash," said Darkey.

"Don't interrupt. Well, five of these gay little dolls wanted to go to Hong Kong, and they arranged with the Chinese sailors to stow away; I believe their friends paid those cold-blooded fiends

ends something to pass them down food on the voyage and give
hem an airing at nights. We had a particularly lively trip,
attened everything down tight, and scarcely uncovered till we got
ito port. Then I and another man found those five girls among
he coal."

" Dead, eh ? "

" They'd simply torn themselves to pieces. Their bits of frock
hings were in strips, and they were scratched deep from top to
oe. The Chinese had never troubled their heads about them at
ll, although they must have known it meant death. You may
et there was a row. The Japanese authorities make you search
hip before sailing, now."

" Well ? "

" Well, I sha'n't die like that. That's all."

He stretched himself out once more, and for ten minutes
either spoke. The park-keeper strolled up again.

" Get up, there ! " he said shortly and gruffly.

" Up ye get, mate," added Darkey, but the man on the bench
id not stir. One look at his face sufficed to startle the keeper,
nd presently two policemen were wheeling an ambulance cart to
he hospital. Darky followed, gave such information as he could,
nd then went his own ways.

II

In the afternoon the patient regained full consciousness. His
yes wandered vacantly about the illimitable ward, with its rows of
eds stretching away on either side of him. A woman with a
vhite cap, a white apron, and white wristbands bent over him,
nd he felt something gratefully warm passing down his throat.

For

For just one second he was happy. Then his memory returned, and the nurse saw that he was crying. When he caught the nurse's eye he ceased, and looked steadily at the distant ceiling.

"You're better?"

"Yes." He tried to speak boldly, decisively, nonchalantly. He was filled with a sense of physical shame, the shame which bodily helplessness always experiences in the presence of arrogant, patronising health. He would have got up and walked briskly away if he could. He hated to be waited on, to be humoured, to be examined and theorised about. This woman would be wanting to feel his pulse. She should not ; he would turn cantankerous. No doubt they had been saying to each other, "And so young, too ! How sad !" Confound them.

"Have you any friends that you would like to send for?"

"No, none."

The girl (she was only a girl) looked at him, and there was that in her eye which overcame him.

"None at all?"

"Not that I want to see."

"Are your parents alive?"

"My mother is, but she lives away in the North."

"You've not seen her lately, perhaps?"

He did not reply, and the nurse spoke again, but her voice sounded indistinct and far off.

When he awoke it was night. At the other end of the ward was a long table covered with a white cloth, and on this table a lamp.

In the ring of light under the lamp was an open book, an inkstand and a pen. A nurse (not *his* nurse) was standing by the table, her fingers idly drumming the cloth, and near her a man in evening dress. Perhaps a doctor. They were conversing in low tones.

tones. In the middle of the ward was an open stove, and the restless flames were reflected in all the brass knobs of the bedsteads and in some shining metal balls which hung from an unlighted chandelier. His part of the ward was almost in darkness. A confused, subdued murmur of little coughs, breathings, rustlings, was continually audible, and sometimes it rose above the conversation at the table. He noticed all these things. He became conscious, too, of a strangely familiar smell. What was it? Ah, yes! Acetic acid—his mother used it for her rheumatics.

Suddenly, magically, a great longing came over him. He must see his mother, or his brothers, or his little sister—some one who knew him, some one who *belonged* to him. He could have cried out in his desire. This one thought consumed all his faculties. If his mother could but walk in just now through that doorway! If only old Spot, even, could amble up to him, tongue out and tail furiously wagging! He tried to sit up, and he could not move! Then despair settled on him, and weighed him down. He closed his eyes.

The doctor and the nurse came slowly up the ward, pausing here and there. They stopped before his bed, and he held his breath.

" Not roused up again, I suppose ? "

" No."

" Hm ! He may flicker on for forty-eight hours. Not more."

They went on, and with a sigh of relief he opened his eyes again. The doctor shook hands with the nurse, who returned to the table and sat down.

Death! The end of all this! Yes, it was coming. He felt it. His had been one of those wasted lives of which he used to read in books. How strange! Almost amusing! He was one of those sons who bring sorrow and shame into a family. Again, how

how strange! What a coincidence that he, just *he* and not
the man in the next bed, should be one of those rare, legendary
good-for-nothings who go recklessly to ruin. And yet, he
was sure that he was not such a bad fellow after all. Only
somehow he had been careless. Yes, careless, that was the
word . . . . nothing worse. . . . . As to death, he was indifferent. Remembering his father's death, he reflected that it
was probably less disturbing to die oneself than to watch
another pass.

He smelt the acetic acid once more, and his thoughts reverted
to his mother. Poor mother! No, great mother! The
grandeur of her life's struggle filled him with a sense of awe.
Strange that until that moment he had never seen the heroic
side of her humdrum, commonplace existence! He must
write to her, now, at once, before it was too late. His
letter would trouble her, add another wrinkle to her face, but
he must write; she must know that he had been thinking of
her.

"Nurse," he cried out, in a thin, weak voice.

"Ssh!" She was by his side directly, but not before he had lost
consciousness again.

The following morning he managed with infinite labour to
scrawl a few lines :

"DEAR MAMMA,

"You will be surprised but not glad to get this letter.
I'm done for, and you will never see me again. I'm sorry for
what I've done, and how I've treated you, but it's no use saying
anything now. If Pater had only lived he might have kept me
in order. But you were too kind, you know. You've had a
hard struggle these last six years, and I hope Arthur and
Dick

Dick will stand by you better than I did, now they are growing up. Give them my love, and kiss little Fannie for me.

"WILLIE."

"Mrs. Hancock——"

He got no further with the address.

III

By some strange turn of the wheel, Darkey gathered several shillings during the next day or two, and feeling both elated and benevolent, he called one afternoon at the hospital, "just to inquire like." They told him the man was dead.

"By the way, he left a letter without an address. Mrs. Hancock—here it is."

"That'll be his mother ; he did tell me about her—lived at Endon, Staffordshire, he said. I'll see to it."

They gave Darkey the letter.

"So his name's Hancock," he soliloquised, when he got into the street. "I knew a girl of that name—once. I'll go and have a pint of four half."

At nine o'clock that night Darkey was still consuming four half, and relating certain adventures by sea which, he averred, had happened to himself. He was very drunk.

"Yes," he said, "and them five lil' gals was lying there without a stitch on 'em, dead as meat ; 's'true as I'm 'ere. I've seen a thing or two in my time, I can tell ye."

"Talking about these Anarchists——" said a man who appeared anxious to change the subject.

"An—kists," Darkey interrupted. "I tell ye what I'd do with

with that muck." He stopped to light his pipe, looked in vain
for a match, felt in his pockets, and pulled out a piece of paper—
the letter.

"I tell you what I'd do. I'd——" He slowly and meditatively tore the letter in two, dropped one piece on the floor,
thrust the other into a convenient gas jet, and applied it to the
tobacco.

"I'd get 'em 'gether in a heap and I'd—— Damn this
pipe." He picked up the other half of the letter, and relighted
the pipe.

"After you, mate," said a man sitting near, who was just
biting the end from a cigar.

A Sonnet

By William Watson

The Frontier

AT the hushed brink of twilight,—when, as though
    Some solemn journeying phantom paused to lay
An ominous finger on the awestruck day,
Earth holds her breath till that great presence go,—
A moment comes of visionary glow,
Pendulous 'twixt the gold hour and the grey,
Lovelier than these, more eloquent than they
Of memory, foresight, and life's ebb and flow.

So have I known, in some fair woman's face,
While viewless yet was Time's more gross imprint,
The first, faint, hesitant, elusive hint
Of that invasion of the vandal years
Seem deeper beauty than youth's cloudless grace,
    Wake subtler dreams, and touch me nigh to tears.

A Marriage

By Ella D'Arcy

I

IN the upstairs room of a City restaurant two young men were
finishing their luncheon. They had taken the corner table
by the window, and as it was past two o'clock the room was
fairly empty. There being no one at either of the tables next
them, they could talk at their ease.

West, the elder of the two, was just lighting a cigarette. The
other, Catterson, who, in spite of a thin moustache, looked little
more than a boy, had ordered a cup of black coffee. When even
a younger man than he was at present, he had passed a couple
of years in Paris, and he continued, by the manner in which he
wore his hair, by his taste in neckties, and by his preferences in
food and drink, to pay Frenchmen the sincerest flattery that was
in his power.

But to-day he let the coffee stand before him untasted. His
young forehead was pushed up into horizontal lines, his full-lipped
mouth was slightly open with anxious, suspended breath. He
gazed away, through the red velvet lounges, through the gilt-
framed mirrors, to the distant object of his thought.

West, leaning back in his seat, emitting arabesques and spirals

of

of brown-grey smoke, watched him with interest rather than with sympathy, and could not repress a smile when Catterson, coming abruptly out of dreamland, turned towards him, to say : " You see, if it were only for the child's sake, I feel I ought to marry her, and the next may be a boy. I should like him to inherit the little property, small as it is. And I've no power to will it."

His voice was half decided, wholly interrogative, and West smiled. There had been a moment in all their conversations of the last six weeks, when some such remark from Catterson was sure to fall. Experience enabled West to anticipate its arrival, and he smiled to find his anticipation so accurately fulfilled.

" My dear chap, I see you're going to do it," he answered, " so it's useless for me to protest any more. But I'll just remind you of an old dictum, which, maybe, you'll respect, because it's in French : ' Ne faites jamais de votre maîtresse, votre femme.'"

West spoke lightly, uttering the quotation just because it happened to flash through his mind ; but all the same, it was a fixed idea of his, that if you married a girl of " that sort," she was sure to discover, sooner or later, colossal vices ; she was sure to kick over the traces, to take to drink, or to some other form of dissipation.

Catterson shrugged his shoulders, flushed, and frowned ; then recovered his temper, and began again, stammeringly, tumultuously, his words tripping over one another in their haste. He always stammered a little in moments of emotion.

" But you d-don't know Nettie. She's not at all—s-she's quite different from what you think. Until she had the misfortune to meet with me, she was as good a girl as you could find."

" No, I don't know her, I admit," observed West, and smoked in silence.

" I have been thinking," Catterson said presently, " that I should
like

like you to come down to see her. I should like you to make her acquaintance, because then I am sure you would agree I am right. I do want to have your support and approval, you know."

West smiled again. It amused him to note the anxiety Catterson exhibited for his approval and support, yet he knew all the time that the young man was bent on marrying Nettie Hooper in spite of anything he could say.

But he understood the springs of the apparent contradiction. He understood Catterson fairly well, without being fond of him. They had been schoolmates. Chance lately, rather than choice on West's side, had again thrown them together ; now the luncheon hour saw them in almost daily companionship. And, correcting his earlier impressions of the impulsive, sensitive, volatile little boy by these more recent ones, he read Catterson's as a weak, amiable, and affectionate nature ; he saw him always anxious to stand well with his associates, to be liked and looked up to by his little world. To do as others do, was his ruling passion ; what Brown, Jones, and Robinson might say of him, his first consideration. It was because at one time Robinson, Jones, and Brown had been represented for him by a circle of gay young Frenchmen that he had thought it incumbent upon him, when opportunity offered, to tread in their footsteps. It was because he found his path set now within the respectable circles of British middle-class society, that his anomalous position was becoming a burden ; that the double personality of married man and father in his riverside lodgings, of eligible bachelor in the drawing-rooms of Bayswater and Maida Vale, grew daily more intolerable to sustain. He could think of no easier way out of the dilemma than to make Nettie his wife, and let the news gradually leak out, that he had been married for the last two years.

Some

Some of his arguments in favour of the marriage—and he required many arguments to outweigh his consciousness of the *mésalliance*—were that, for all practical purposes, he was as good as married already. He could never give Nettie up ; he must always provide for her and the child as long as he lived. And his present mode of life was full of inconveniences. He was living at Teddington under an assumed name, and it is not at all pleasant to live under an assumed name. At any moment one may be discovered, and an awkward situation may result.

These were some of his arguments. But then, too, he had developed the domestic affections to a surprising degree, and if his first passion for Nettie were somewhat assuaged, he had a much more tender feeling for her now than in the beginning. And he was devoted to his little daughter ; a devotion which a few months ago he would have sworn he was incapable of feeling for any so uninteresting an animal as a baby. He reproached himself bitterly for having placed her at such a disadvantage in life as illegitimacy entails ; he felt that he ought at least to give the expected child all the rights which a legal recognition can confer.

His chief argument, however, was that he had sinned, and that in marriage lay the only reparation ; and let a man persuade himself that a certain course of action is the one righteous, the one honourable course to take—more particularly if it jumps with his own private inclinations—and nothing can deter him from it.

"Not even French proverbs," laughed West into his beard.

"Come down and see her," Catterson urged, and West, moved by a natural curiosity, as well as by a desire to oblige his friend, agreed to meet him that evening at Waterloo, that they might go down together.

His soul being eased through confession, Catterson regained at once the buoyant good spirits which were natural to him, but which,

which, of late, secret anxieties and perturbation of mind had overshadowed completely. For when depressed he touched deeper depths of depression than his neighbour, in exact proportion to the unusual height and breadth of his gaiety in his moments of elation.

Now he enlivened the journey out from town, by cascades of exuberant talk, filling up the infrequent pauses with snatches of love-songs : the music-hall love-songs of the day.

Yet as the train approached Teddington, he fell into silence again. A new anxiety began to dominate him : the anxiety that West should be favourably impressed by Nettie Hooper. His manner became more nervous, his stammer increased ; a red spot burned on either cheek. He could not keep his thoughts or his speech from the coming interview.

"She doesn't talk much," he explained, as they walked along the summer sunset roads ; "she's very shy ; but you mustn't on that account imagine she's not glad to see you. She's very much interested in you. She wants to meet you very much."

"Of course she's not what's called a lady," he began again ; "her people don't count at all. She, herself, wants to drop them. But you would never discover she wasn't one. She has a perfect accent, a perfect pronunciation. And she is so wonderfully modest and refined. I assure you, I've known very few real ladies to compare to her."

He eulogised her economy, her good management. "My money goes twice as far since she has had the spending of it. She's so clever, and you can't think how well she cooks. She has learned it from the old lady with whom we lodge. Mrs. Baker is devoted to Nettie, would do anything for her, thinks there's no one like her in the world. And then she makes all her own clothes, and is better dressed than any girl I see, although they only cost her a few shillings."

He

He sang the praises of her sweetness, of her gentleness, of her domesticity. "She's so absolutely unselfish; such a devoted mother to our little girl; and yet, she's scarcely more than a child herself. She won't be nineteen till next April."

All which encomiums and dozens more wearied West's ear, without giving him any clear conception of their subject. He was thankful when Catterson suddenly broke off with, "Here we are, this is Rose Cottage."

West saw the usual, creeper-covered, French-windowed, sham-romantic, and wholly dilapidated little villa, which realises the ideal of all young lovers for a first nest. To more prosaic minds it suggested earwigs and spiders in summer, loose tiles and burst pipes in winter, and general dampness and discomfort all the year round.

It stood separated from the road by a piece of front garden, in which the uncut grass waved fairy spear-heads, and the unpruned bushes matted out so wide and thick, as to screen off completely the sitting-room from the passers-by.

The narrow gravel path leading up to the door was painted with mosses, the little trellis-work porch was giving way beneath the weight of vine-wood and rose-stem which lay heavy upon it; the virginia-creeper over the window-top swayed down to the ground in graceful diminishing tresses; the bedroom windows above blinked tiny eyes beneath heavy eyelids of greenery. An auctioneer would have described the place as a bijou bower of verdure, and West's sense of humour was tickled by the thoroughly conventional background it provided for the conventional *solitude à deux*.

Catterson rang that he might give notice of West's arrival, and a thin bell responded to his pull from the interior of the house. It was succeeded by the tapping of high heels along the oilcloth,

the

the door opened, and a very little woman, in a dark woollen gown, stood within the threshold.

The nurse, the landlady, the servant, perhaps? West told himself that *this* could not be Nettie Hooper, this plain little creature, who was surely so much older than the girl Catterson had described.

But the next instant Catterson said, " Nettie, this is my great friend, West," and the little woman had given him a lifeless hand, while she welcomed him in curious, drawling tones, " I'm so glad to see you ; Jack is always talking about you ; do come in."

He was certain she was plain, but he had no time to localise her plainness—to decide whether it lay in feature, complexion, or expression, for her back was towards him ; he was following her into the sitting-room, and he looked down upon a dark head of hair, a meagre figure, a dowdy home-made gown.

" I hope you've got a good dinner for us," Catterson began at once, stammering over every consonant. " I don't know how West may be feeling, but I'm uncommonly hungry myself."

" You didn't give me much time," she answered ; " your wire only came at four. I've got you some fish, and a steak."

" And a salad? good ! Nettie's steaks are ripping, West, you'll see."

" Oh, but Mrs. Baker is going to cook the dinner to-night ; I didn't think you'd wish me to leave you and Mr. West, like that."

During these not very illuminating remarks, West was revising his first impressions. He confessed that the girl had nice features, regular, well-proportioned ; that, though she lacked colour, her complexion was of a healthy paleness ; that her expression could hardly be called disagreeable, for the difficulty lay in deciding whether she had any expression at all. All the same, she was plain ; flat-chested, undeveloped, with clumsy feet and hands.

" You

"You have a—quiet little place here," he said to her to make conversation. He had been going to say "a charming, little place," but a glance round the dark, musty-smelling room was too much for his powers of unveracity.

"Yes, it's almost too quiet, while Jack is away. Don't you think, Mr. West, I'm very good to stay here by myself all day long?"

She had the oddest voice, very drawling, measured, inanimate. It said nothing at all to the listener beyond the mere actual words.

"Come, you've got baby," said Catterson, laughing, "let alone Mrs. Baker."

"As though one's landlady and a baby of seventeen months were all the companionship one could require!" She laughed too.

She was almost pretty when she laughed, and West began to perceive that after all she might be no older than Catterson had said. She had the abundant crisp-growing hair, the irreproachable smoothness of skin found only in youth's company. Her eyes were really remarkable eyes, large, of a bluish-grey, clear as water, with the pupils very big.

Yes, she was exceedingly pretty. It took you some time to see it perhaps, but once you had seen it you wondered you could have overlooked it before. Yet West had no sooner admitted the fact than he began to qualify it. He said there was absolutely nothing in her face that appealed to your imagination; that such very limpid eyes go with a cold or a shallow nature, that such very large pupils denote either want of intelligence or want of strength.

And there was undeniably something common in her physiognomy, though at first he could not decide in which particular trait it lay. Was it in the cut of the nostril, the line of the mouth? No, he thought it was to be found, rather, in a certain

certain unpleasing shininess of surface. Her cheek had less of the velvety texture of the peach, than the glaze of the white-heart cherry. The wings of the nose, its slightly aquiline bridge, reflected the light in little patches.

If her hair was unusually thick, it was coarse too, and of a uniform dark-brown colour. The front, cut short, seemed to rebel against the artificial curling to which it was subjected. Instead of lying on her forehead in rings as was no doubt intended, here was an undistinguishable fuzz, while there a straight mesh stood out defiantly.

She had pretty ears and execrably ugly hands, in the thick fingers of which, with squat nails broader than they were long, in the tough and wrinkled skin, the want of race of her ancestors was easily to be read. On the left hand she wore a plain gold ring.

So soon as the first fillip or greeting was spent, she became noticeable for her silences; had a way of letting every subject drop; and expressed no opinions, or only those universal ones which every woman may express without danger of self-revelation. For instance, when West asked whether she cared for reading, she said she was passionately fond of it; but when pressed as to what she liked best to read, she mentioned, after considerable hesitation, *East Lynne* and *Shakespeare*.

As Catterson had said, there was no fault to find with her pronunciation or her accent; or what faults there were, were faults he himself was guilty of. West realised that she was quick in imitation, and, up to a certain point, receptive. She had carefully modelled her deportment on Catterson's, held her knife and fork, lifted her glass, and used her table napkin in precisely the same way he did. When, later on, West had occasion to see her handwriting he found it a curiously close copy of Catterson's own.

Women,

Women, whose characters are still undeveloped, and whose writing therefore remains unformed, almost invariably do adopt, for a time, the handwriting of their lovers.

There was nothing in her manners or appearance, to indicate her precise social origin, nor did West, by-the-by, ever learn anything definite concerning it. Catterson was very sensitive on the point, and only once made the vaguest, the most cursory reference to how he had met her.

Still less was there anything about Nettie Hooper to fit in with West's preconceived theories. As she sat there, placid, silent, quiet, he had to admit that as Catterson had said, she was not at all the sort of girl he had imagined her to be. And yet . . . .

He made the above mental notes during the course of the dinner, while Catterson's nervousness gradually wore off, and his gaiety returned. His infatuation for Nettie, led him, when in her presence, to the conviction that every one else must be equally infatuated too.

The dining-room was small, and like the parlour looked out through a French window over a tangled slip of garden. The furniture consisted chiefly of Japanese fans, but there was also a round table, and at least three chairs. The arrangements, generally, were of a picnic character, and when Mrs. Baker, a stout and loquacious old body, brought in the dishes, she stayed awhile to join in the conversation, addressing them all impartially as " My dear," and Nettie in particular as " My dear Life."

But the meal if simple, was satisfying, and Nettie herself left the table to make the coffee, as Catterson had taught her to do, in French fashion. He brought out from the chiffoniere a bottle of green Chartreuse, and Nettie handed cigarettes and found an ashtray. She was full of ministering attentions.

While they smoked and talked, and she sat silent, her limpid eyes

eyes fixed mostly on Catterson, although every now and then, West knew they were turned upon him, wails were heard from upstairs.

"It's baby, poor little soul," said Nettie, rising. "Please, Jack, may I go and bring her down?"

She presently returned with a flannel-gowned infant in her arms. The child had just the same large, limpid, blue-grey eyes as the mother, with just the same look in them. She fixed West with the relentless, unswerving stare of childhood, and not all her father's blandishments could extract a smile.

Nettie, kissing the square-toed, pink feet, addressed her as "Blossom," and "Dear little soul," then sat tranquilly nursing her, as a child might nurse a doll.

She had really many of a child's ways, and when Catterson, at the end of the evening, put on his hat to accompany West to the station, she asked in her long, plaintive drawl, "May I come, too, Jack?" exactly as a child asks permission of parent or master. She put her head back again into the dining-room a moment after leaving it. "What shall I put on, my cloak or my cape?" she said; "and must I change my shoes?"

Catterson turned to West with a smile, which asked for congratulations. "You see how docile she is, how gentle? And it's always the same. It's always my wishes that guide her. She never does anything without asking my opinion and advice. I don't know how a man could have a better wife. I know I should never find one to suit me better. But now you've seen her for yourself, you've come over to my opinion, I feel sure? You've got nothing further to urge against my marrying her, have you?"

West was saved the embarrassment of a reply by the reappearance of Nettie in outdoor things, and Catterson was too satisfied

in

A Marriage

in his own mind with the effect she must have produced, to notice the omission.

He talked gaily on indifferent matters until the train moved out of the station, and West carried away with him a final vignette of the two young people standing close together beneath the glare of a gas-lamp, Catterson with an arm affectionately slipped through the girl's. His thin, handsome face was flushed with excitement and self-content. The demure little figure beside him, that did not reach up to his shoulder, in neat black coat and toque, stared across the platform up to West, from limpid, most curious eyes.

What the devil was the peculiarity of those eyes, he asked himself impatiently? and hammered out the answer to the oscillations of the carriage, the vibration of the woodwork, the flicker of the lamp, as the train rumbled through the night and jerked up at flaring stations.

Beautiful as to shape and colour, beautiful in their fine dark lashes, in their thinly pencilled brows, these strange eyes seemed to look at you and ostentatiously to keep silence; to thrust you coldly back, to gaze through you and beyond you, as if with the set purpose of avoiding any explanation with your own.

It was this singularity which in the shock of first sight had repelled, which had shed over the face an illusory plainness, which had suggested age and experience, so that it had taken West an appreciable time to discover that Nettie Hooper was in reality quite young, and exceedingly pretty. But he had learned on a dozen previous occasions, that the first instantaneous, unbiased impression is the one to be trusted. Especially in so far as concerns the eyes. The eyes are very literally the windows of the soul.

Three

II

Three years later, West and two men who don't come into this story at all, were spending the month of August up the river. An ill-advised proceeding, for the weather, so far, had proved deplorably wet, as the weather in August too often does, and of all sad places in wet weather, the river is incomparably the saddest.

But they had hired their boat, they had made their arrangements, dates were fixed, and places decided on. With the thoroughly British mental twist that to change your plans is to show inconsistency, and therefore weakness, West's companions were determined to carry these plans out to their prearranged end.

He scoffed at their mulishness, but submitted nevertheless ; and following their example he rowed with bent head and set teeth through the continually falling rain, or sat, in their society during interminable hours waiting for it to cease, in an open boat beneath a dripping elm-tree. And as he gazed out over the leaden sheet of pock-marked water, he found amusement in telling himself that here at least was a typically national way of taking a holiday.

Nor, after all, did it always rain. There were occasional days of brilliant, if unstable sunshine, when the stream ran dimpling between its banks of sweet flag and loose-strife ; when the sand-martins skimmed over the water with their pittering cry ; when the dabchick, as the boat stole upon her, dived so suddenly, remained under for so long, and rose again so far off, that but for a knowledge of her habits, you would pronounce it a genuine case of bird suicide.

It was on one such a sunny, inspiriting Saturday, that a twenty mile

mile pull from Maidenhead brought them by afternoon in sight of the picturesque old bridge at Sonning. Here, in Sonning, they were to pass the night and stay over till Monday. For here one of the men had an aunt, and he was under strict maternal orders to dine with her on Sunday.

There was the usual difference of opinion as to which of the two inns they should put up at, the White Hart being voted too noisy, the French Horn condemned as too swagger. But the question was settled by the White Hart, which you reach first on the Berkshire bank, proving full ; they accordingly pulled round the mill-water on the right, to try their luck at the French Horn.

For those who do not know it, this may be described as one of the prettiest of riverside inns ; a cosy-looking, two-storied house, with a wide verandah, and a lawn sloping down to the water's edge. Beneath the trees on either side, tea was set out on wicker tea-tables, and each table had its encircling group of gay frocks and scarlet sunshades. It presented a Watteau-like picture of light and shadow and colour, the artistic value of which was increased by three conspicuous figures, which took the spectator's eye straight to the centre of the foreground.

A man, a girl, and a little child stood together, just above the wooden landing-steps, and a Canadian canoe, brilliant with new-ness and varnish, flaring with flame-coloured cushions, rocked gently on the water at their feet.

The young man held the painter in his hand ; was dressed in immaculate white flannel, wore a pink and white striped shirt, and a waist-handkerchief of crimson silk.

The girl was the boating-girl of the stage. Where the rushes fringed the lawn you looked instinctively for footlights. The open-work silk stockings, the patent leather evening shoes, the silver

belt

belt compressing a waist of seventeen inches, were all so thoroughly theatrical. So was her costume of pale blue and white ; so was the knot of broad ribbon fastening her sailor collar ; so was the Jack Tar cap, with its blue and silver binding, set slightly on one side of her dark head. The child by her side was dressed in white embroidered muslin and a sun-bonnet.

" I say, West," cried the man who steered, " you who know all the actresses, tell us who's that little girl there, with the kid."

West, who was sculling, turned his head.

" Oh, damn ! it's Mrs. Catterson," he said, with the emphasis of a surprise, which is a disagreeable one.

Since the marriage, he had not seen very much of Nettie Catterson, although he was godfather to the boy. For one thing, it is difficult to see much of people who live in the suburbs ; and though Catterson had moved twice, first from Teddington to Kingston, then from Kingston to Surbiton Hill, where he was now a householder, Surbiton remained equally out of West's way.

But there was another reason for his evasion of the constant invitations which Catterson pressed upon him in the City. It had not taken him long to perceive that he was far from being *persona grata* to Mrs. Catterson. Whether this was to be accounted for by the average woman's inevitable jealousy of her husband's friends, whether it was she suspected his opposition to her marriage, or whether she could not forgive him for having known her while she was passing as Mrs. Grey, he could not determine. Probably her dislike was compounded of all three reasons, with a preponderance, he thought, in favour of the last.

For with marriage, the possession of a semi-detatched villa at Surbiton, and the entrance into such society as a visit from the clergyman's wife may open the door to, Nettie had become of an amazing conventionality, and surpassing Catterson himself

in

in the matter of deference to Mrs. Grundy, she seemed to
have set herself the task of atoning for irregularity of conduct
in the past, by the severest reprobation of all who erred in the
present, and West's ribaldry in conversation, his light views on
serious subjects, and his habitual desecration of the Sunday were
themes for her constant animadversions and displeasure.

It was the rapid *résumé* of these, his demerits with Mrs. Catterson, which had called forth his energetic " Damn ! "

At the same moment that he recognised her, Catterson
recognised him, and sung out a welcome. The boat was brought
alongside, and he was received by Nettie with a warmth which
surprised him. His companions, with hasty cap-lifting, escaped
across the lawn to get drinks at the bar, and secure beds for the
night.

He looked after them with envy ; and had to accept Nettie's
invitation to tea.

" We were just quarrelling, Jack and I," she said, " where to
have it. He wants to go down to Marlow, and I want it here.
Now you've come, that settles it. We'll have it here."

Catterson explained his reason : as Nettie wished to go out in
the canoe again, they ought to go now while it was fine, as it was
sure to rain later.

Nettie denied the possibility of rain with an asperity which
informed West that he had arrived on the crest of a domestic
disagreement, and he understood at once the cordiality of his
reception.

She had developed none of the tempestuous views which his
theories had required ; on the contrary she appeared to be just
the ordinary wife, with the ordinary contempt for her husband's
foibles and wishes. She could talk of the trials of housekeeping
and the iniquities of servants as to the manner born, and always

imitative

imitative had lately given back the ideals of Surbiton with the
fidelity of a mirror. But there were curious undercurrents
beneath this surface smoothness, of which West now and then got
an indication.

He renewed his acquaintance with Gladys, the little girl, who
periodically forgot him, and asked after his godson. But the
subject proved unfortunate.

Nettie's mouth took menacing lines. "Cyril, I'm sorry to say,
is a very naughty boy. I don't know what we're going to do
with him, I'm sure."

West couldn't help smiling. "It's somewhat early days to
despair of his ultimate improvement, perhaps? How old is he?
Not three till December, I think?" He told himself that the
open-hearted, sensitive, impulsive little fellow ought not to be very
difficult to manage.

"He's old enough to be made to obey," she said, with a glance
at Catterson, which suggested some contentious background to the
remark.

"Oh, well, one doesn't want to break the child's spirit," Catterson protested.

"I think his spirit will have to be broken very soon," asserted
Nettie, "if he goes on being as troublesome as he has been
lately."

Gladys, sitting by her mother's side, drank in everything that
was said. She was now five years old, and a little miniature of
Nettie. She turned her clear and stolid eyes from one to another.
"Cyril's a . . . . naughty . . . . little boy," she observed in
a piping drawl, a thin exaggeration of Nettie's own, and making
impressive pauses between the words. "He's never going to be
tooked . . . . up the river like me. Is he, mother?"

"If you want to be a good little girl," observed Catterson,
                                                    "you'll

"you'll put your bread and jam into your mouth, instead of feeding your ear with it as you are doing at present."

"Cyril don't have . . . . no jam . . . . for *his* tea," she began again, "'cos he's so naughty. He only has dry bread an'——"

"Come, come, don't talk so much, Gladys," said her father impatiently, "or perhaps you won't get 'tooked' up the river again either."

Nettie put an arm round her.

"Poor little soul! Mother'll take her up the river always, won't she? We don't mind what Papa says, do we?"

"Silly old Papa!" cried the child, throwing him one of Nettie's own looks, "we don't mind what he says, we don't."

All the same, when tea was over, and they prepared to make a start in the canoe, West their still somewhat unwilling guest, Catterson put his foot down and refused to take Gladys with them for various reasons. Four couldn't get into the canoe with safety or comfort; the child had been out all day, and had already complained of sickness from the constant swaying motion; but chiefly because it was undoubtedly going to rain. Nettie gave in with a bad grace, and the little girl was led off, roaring, by her maid.

Nettie had complained that the tea was cold, and that she could not drink it. She had insisted on Catterson having a second brew brought. Then when this came had pushed away her cup, and pronounced it as unpalatable as before. But no sooner were they some way down stream, than she said she was thirsty, and asked for ginger beer.

West remembered Catterson telling him long ago, how Nettie would suddenly wake up thirsty in the middle of the night, and how he would have to get up and go down to forage for something to quench her thirst. It had seemed to Catterson, in those

those days, very amusing, pathetic, and childlike, and he had told of it with evident relish and pride. But the little perversity which is so attractively provoking in the young girl, often comes to provoke without any attractiveness in the wife and mother.

Catterson turned the canoe when Nettie spoke, saying they had best go and get what she wanted at the White Hart, but West fancied he looked annoyed and slightly ashamed.

After this little episode, because of the ominous appearance of the sky, it was agreed to keep up stream towards the lock. But before they reached it the first great drops of rain were splashing into the water about them. The lock-keeper made them welcome. He and Catterson were old acquaintances. Having set out for them, and dusted down three Windsor chairs, he went to spread a tarpaulin over the canoe.

The darkness of the little room grew deeper every instant. Then came an illuminating flash followed by a shattering thunder-peal. The ear was filled with the impetuous downrush of the rain.

"There! Why wouldn't you let me bring Gladys?" cried Nettie. "Poor little soul, she's so terrified of thunder, she'll scream herself into fits."

"She's right enough with Annie," said Catterson, somewhat too confidently.

Nettie replied that Annie was a perfect fool, more afraid of a storm than the child herself. "Jack, you'll have to go back and comfort her. Jack, you *must* go!"

"My dear, in this rain!" he expostulated. "How can you want me to do anything so mad?"

But Nettie had worked herself up into a paroxysm of maternal solicitude, of anguish of mind. West asked himself if it were entirely genuine, or partly a means of punishing Catterson for his self-assertion a while ago.

"Since

"Since you're so afraid of a little rain," she concluded contemptuously, "I'll go myself.   I'm not going to let the child die in hysterics."

She made a movement as though to leave the house.   Catterson drew her back, and turning up the collar of his coat, went out. But before the canoe was fairly launched, West knew he must be wet to the skin.   He stood and watched him paddling down against the closely serried, glittering lances of the rain, until lost in a haze of watery grey.

Then, for his life, he could not refrain from speaking. "I think it's very unwise for Jack to get wet like that. It's not as though he were particularly strong.   He comes of a delicate, short-lived family, as you probably know?"

But Nettie only stared silently before her as though she had not heard.

And there, in silence, they remained for another twenty minutes, while the rain flooded earth and river, and the thunder rumbled to and fro over the sky.

Nettie maintained an absolute silence, and West, leaning against the window-frame, beguiled the time in studying her with fleeting, inoffensive glances.   He again noted the ugliness of her hands, to which, as they lay folded in her lap, the flashing of a half-hoop of fine diamonds, now worn above the wedding-ring, carried first his attention.   But when he raised his eyes to her small, pale face, he decided she was prettier than she used to be, more strikingly pretty at first sight.   She had learned, perhaps, to bring out her better points.   He thought she dressed her hair more becomingly ;   three years steady application of curling irons had at last induced it to lie in softer curls.   Five years of married life had in no wise dimmed the transparency of her skin.   Not a line recorded an emotion whether of pleasure or of pain.   If she
had

had lived through any psychic experiences, they had not left the faintest mark behind. And it was partly the immobility of countenance by which this smoothness of surface was maintained, which led West again to qualify his favourable verdict, just as he had done before.

He began to think that the predominant note in her character was coldness, heartlessness even. He remembered, not so long ago, hearing her relate as though it were a good story, how meeting old Mrs. Baker one day in Kingston Market, she had passed her by with an unrecognising stare. Yet the old woman had been devoted to Nettie, as she herself used to boast; a certain feeling of gratitude, of kindliness might have been looked for in return.

But there must have been others, West told himself, to whom she owed a greater debt—the relations, or friends, who had brought her up, clothed her and fed her until the day she had met with Catterson. She never referred to these others, she never let slip the smallest allusion to her early life ; she held her secrets with a tenacity which was really uncommon ; but it was evident that she had turned her back on all who had ever befriended her with the same cold ease she had shown to Mrs. Baker.

She was fond, apparently, of her little girl, but this particular affection was no contradiction to her general want of it ; she saw in the child a reduplication of herself. For Gladys was the image of her mother, just as the little boy was Catterson over again ; very nervous, sensitive, and eager for love and approval.

West mused over the curious want of sympathy Nettie had always displayed for the boy. It amounted almost to dislike. He had never been able to win her good word from the day of his birth, and his natural timidity was greatly augmented by her

severe

severe treatment. West was inclined to believe the reason to be a sort of jealousy for Gladys ; that she resented the fact that Cyril was legitimate ; that he would inherit under his grandfather's will, while the little girl, the first born, the preferred child, could not.

Catterson had never alluded to the subject, but for all that West knew that he was profoundly hurt by the difference Nettie made between the children. If he himself made any in his heart, and West said it would be only natural if he loved Cyril most, who adored his father and impulsively showed it, rather than Gladys who always coldly repulsed his overtures of affection, at least in his conduct towards them he never let it appear. He even seemed to overlook Cyril a little, having learned by experi-ence probably, what were the consequences of paying him too much attention. Cyril was always left at home, while Gladys accompanied her parents everywhere.

Studying Nettie's physiognomy, tracing the lines of the mouth, the slightly backward drawn nostrils, the hard insensitive hands, West found himself rejoicing he did not stand in his poor little godson's shoes.

The storm was over, the sun was out again, and Nettie rising suggested they should go. They crossed over the top of the lock gates, picked their way between the puddles of the towing-path and so back over Sonning Bridge to the hotel.

Catterson was in his room changing his wet clothes, and Nettie went up to him. West found Gladys sitting in the verandah beside her nurse, tranquilly playing with a doll.

"Well, babe," said he, in friendly tones, "were you very much frightened by the thunder and lightning, just now ? "

But she did not answer, she merely fixed her limpid eyes on his, thrusting him back with their coldly negative stare. Then ostentatiously, she re-absorbed herself in her game.

Th

The next morning kept Catterson in bed with a bad cold and West sooner than pass the day in the vicinity of Nettie, persuaded the nephew to abandon the aunt and the dinner, and both men into the extraordinary inconsistency of pushing on to Streatley.

III

One black morning in December, West remembered, for no reason at all, that it was the birthday of Cyril his godson. Cyril to-day entered on his fifth year, and West found himself making the usual " damned silly reflections " on the flight of time. Dismissing these as stale and unprofitable, he began to wonder what present he could take the boy. He tried to remember what he himself had liked at the age of four, but he could recall nothing of that antediluvian period. He thought of a book, a paint-box, a white fur rabbit, but the delights of painting and reading were surely beyond Cyril's years, while the Bunny was perhaps too infantile. Finally, he set his face westward, trusting to find inspiration in the windows of the shops he passed. The heavenly smell of chocolate which greeted him at Buszard's made him decide on a big packet of bon-bons. He knew from previous experience with the Catterson children, that chocolates were sure to be appreciated.

The Cimmerian morning had dragged its course through brown, orange, and yellow hours, to an afternoon of misty grey. But West nevertheless felt inclined for walking. As he crossed the park diagonally from the Marble Arch to Queen's Gate, his thoughts outran his steps, and were already with the Cattersons.

They had moved again, and now lived in South Kensington.

Nettie

Nettie had become very intimate with a certain Mrs. Reade
whose acquaintance she owed to a week spent in the same hotel.
The two young women had struck up an effusive friendship, based
on a similarity of taste in dress and amusement, Mrs. Reade supply-
ing the model for Nettie's faithful imitation. She copied her
manners, she adopted her opinions and ideas. Mrs. Reade had
declared it was impossible to live so far out of town as Surbiton.
The Cattersons therefore disposed of the lease of their house, and
took one close to Mrs. Reade's in Astwood Place.

Catterson had left his pretty suburban garden with the more
reluctance that he disliked the Reades, considered the husband
common, the wife loud, vulgar, bad style. But he had told West
at the time, there was no price too high to pay for the purchase
of domestic peace.

He was peaceably inclined by nature, but of late, any nervous
energy which might have been contentiously employed was used
up in fighting off the various trifling ailments that continuously
beset him. He was always taking cold; now it was lumbago,
now a touch of congestion, now a touch of pleurisy. He spent
half his days at home in the doctor's hands. Nettie made his bad
health the ostensible reason for quitting Surbiton. The damp air
rising from the river didn't suit him.

Town suited her, as she expressed it, "down to the ground,"
and following in Mrs. Reade's wake, she became one of the
immense crowd of smartly-gowned nobodies, who, always talking
as if they were somebodies, throng fashionable shops, cycle in the
Park, and subscribe to Kensington Town Hall dances. It was
far away from the days when she lived in lodgings at Teddington,
made her own clothes, and cooked her own dinner.

Now she kept four maids, whom she was constantly changing.
West seldom found the door opened by the same girl thrice.
Net

Nettie was an exacting mistress, and had no indulgence for the class from which presumably she had sprung. Her servants were expected to show the perfection of angels, the capacity for work of machines, and the servility of slaves. And she was always detecting imperfections, laziness, or covert impertinence of manner or speech. Every six weeks or so there was a domestic crisis, and Mary or Jane left in tears, and without a character.

West could generally guess from the expression of Jane's or Mary's face how long she had been in Astwood Place. Disappointment, harassment, and sullen discontent were the stages through which each new comer passed before reaching the tearful catastrophe.

From the serene appearance of the young person who to-day let him in, West judged she was but recently arrived. "Mrs. Catterson was out," for which he was not sorry; but "the Master was at home," which he had expected, having heard in the City that Catterson had not been at his office for some days.

He found him huddled up over the drawing-room fire, spreading out his thin hands to the blaze. Half lost in the depths of the armchair, sitting with rounded shoulders and sunken head, he seemed rather some little shrunken sexagenarian than a man still under thirty.

Gladys, with a picture-book open on her knee, sat on a stool against the fender. She did not move as West came in, but raising her eyes considered him, as was her wont, with a steadfast neutrality.

Catterson, turning, jumped up to greet him with something of his old buoyancy of manner; but the change which a few weeks had made in his face gave West a fresh shock. Nor could he disguise it sufficiently quickly—the painful impression.

"You

"You think I'm looking ill, eh?" asserted Catterson, but wi
an eagerness which pleaded for a denial.

West lied instantly and heartily, but Catterson was not taken i

"You think it's all U P with me, I see," he said, returning
the chair, and his former attitude of dejection.

This was so exaggerated a statement of his thoughts that We
tried absolute candour.

"I don't think you're looking very fit," he said; "but wh
you want is change. This dark, damp, beastly weather plays t
deuce with us all. You should run down to Brighton for a fe
days. A man was telling me only last night that Brighton
this week has been just a blaze of sunshine."

"Oh, Brighton!" Catterson repeated, hopelessly, "I'm pa
that." With the finger-tip of one hand he kept probing a
pressing the back of the other as it lay open upon his kne
searching for symptoms of the disease he most dreaded.

To change the channel of his thoughts, West turned to t
little girl who still mutely envisaged him.

"Well, Gladys, have you forgotten, as usual, who I am?"

"No, I haven't . . . . you're Mithter Wetht," she told hi
the piping drawl now complicated by a lisp, due to the fact th
she had lost all her front teeth.

"Where's Sonny?" he asked her. "I've got something f
him," and he put the packet of sweets down on the table by h
elbow.

She reflected a moment as to who Sonny might be; the
"Thyril's a naughty boy," she said. "He'th had a good . .
whipping . . . and hath been put to bed."

"Oh poor old chap!" West exclaimed, ruefully, "and on h
birthday too. What has he done?"

But Gladys only repeated, "He'th a . . . very . . . naugh
                                                    boy

boy," in tones of dogmatic conviction. She seemed to detect the guest's sympathy with the culprit, and to resent it.

Voices and laughter were heard on the stairs. Nettie entered in her bonnet and furs, preceeded by a big, overdressed woman, whom West easily identified as Mrs. Reade. They had been shopping, and both were laden with small, draper's parcels.

Nettie did not seem pleased to find the drawing-room occupied. She gave West a limp hand without looking at him, which was one of her exasperating habits when put out, and then she attacked her husband for keeping up so big a fire. The heat of the room was intolerable, she said; it was enough to make any one ill. She threw off her wraps with an exaggeration of relief, peevishly altered the position of a chair which West had pushed aside inadvertently, and began to move about the room, in the search, as he knew well, of some fresh grievance. Catterson followed her for a second or two with tragic eyes. Then he turned to the fire again. "To me it seems very cold," he murmured; "I've not been warm all day."

Mrs. Reade declared he should take to "byking." That would warm him; there was nothing in the world like it. "Indeed unless it maims you for life, it cures every evil that flesh is heir to."

"But I suppose the chances are in favour of the maiming?" West asked her.

She laughed hilariously at this, and though she was certainly vulgar, as Catterson had complained, West couldn't help liking her. He always did like the women who laughed at his little jokes; (Mrs. Catterson never laughed at them). Besides, she was so obviously healthy and good-natured; handsome too, although you saw that in a few years, she would become too fat.

Nettie wondered why on earth Jack couldn't have had tea

ready,

ready, pulled violently at the bell, and began to examine some
patterns of silk she had brought home with her for the selection
of an evening gown. Her lap was presently filled with little
oblong pieces of black and coloured brocades.

"The green is exquisite, isn't it, Mimi?" she appealed to her
friend, "but do you think it would suit me? Wouldn't it make
me look too pale? The heliotrope is sweet too, but then I had
a gown last year almost that very shade. People would say I
had only had it cleaned or turned. Perhaps, after all, I had
better have black? I've not had a black frock for a long time,
and it's always so smart-looking, isn't it?"

Mrs. Reade thought that in Nettie's place she should choose
the green, and have it made up with myrtle velvet and cream
guipure. An animated discussion of dressmaking details began,
during which the men sat, perforce, silent.

Gladys, meanwhile, had come over to the table on which the
chocolates lay, where she stood, industriously picking open the
paper.

Catterson presently caught sight of this.

"Gladys!" he exclaimed, with the sharp irritability of
ill-health.

She had just popped a fat bon-bon into her mouth, and she
remained petrified for a moment by so unaccustomed a thing as
rebuke. Then for convenience sake, she took the sweet out
again in her thumb and finger, and burst into sobs of anger and
surprise.

Nettie was equally surprised and angry. "What are you
thinking of, Jack, frightening the poor child by shouting at her
like that?"

"But did you see what she was doing, my dear, meddling with
West's property?"

"Mr. We

"Mr. West shouldn't leave his sweets about on the table if he doesn't want the child to have them.   Naturally, she thought they were for her."

"Not at all.   She knew they were for Cyril.   She heard West say so."

"After Cyril's behaviour to me this morning I certainly shall not allow him to have them.   And I don't approve of sweets anyway.   It ruins the children's teeth.   I wish Mr. West wouldn't bring them so often."

This was sufficiently ungracious, and West's answer was sufficiently foolish ; "Perhaps you wish I wouldn't bring myself so often either ? " said he.

"I've no doubt we could manage to get on just as well without you," she retorted, and there were worlds of insult concentrated in the tone.

The only effectual answer would have been immediate departure, but consideration for Catterson held West hesitant.   It is always because of their affection for the husband that the wife finds it so particularly easy, and perhaps so agreeable, to insult his friends. She offers them their choice between perpetual banishment and chunks of humble-pie.

Catterson put an end to the situation himself.

"Let's get away out of this, West," he said, with flushed cheeks and shaking voice, "come down to my study."

Here, the change of atmosphere brought on a fit of coughing, to which West listened with a *serrement de cœur*.   In his mind's eye he saw Catterson again, vividly, as he had been a few years back ; very gay and light-hearted, full of pranks and tricks.   Always restless, always talking, always in tip-top spirits ; when he fell in love, finding expression for the emotion in the whistling and singing of appropriate love-ditties, the music-hall love-ditties of the day.

The

The foolish refrain of one of these recurred to West, ding-dong, pertinaciously at his ear :—

> "They know me well at the County Bank,
>   Cash is better than fame or rank,
>   Then hey go lucky ! I'll marry me ducky,
>   The Belle of the Rose and Crown."

And now Catterson, with pinched features, sunken eyes, and contracted chest, sat there pouring out a flood of bitterness against himself, life, and the gods for the granting of his prayer.

"You remember Nettie before I married her ? Did she not appear the gentlest, the sweetest, the most docile girl in the world ? Who would ever have imagined she could have learned to bully her husband and insult his friends like this ?

"But the moment her position was assured she changed ; changed completely. Why, look here, West, the very day we were married—you remember we went down to Brighton, and were married there—as we walked back along the King's Road, she stopped me before a shop and said, ' You can just come in here and buy me some furs. Now I'm your wife you needn't suppose I'm going through another winter in my wretched, little, old coat of last year.' It was her tone ; the implication of what she had had to endure at my hands, before she had the right to command me. It was the first lifting of the veil on her true character.

"Perhaps if I had never married her—who knows ? Women require to be kept under, to be afraid of you, to live in a condition of insecurity ; to know their good fortune is dependent on their good conduct.

"I did the right thing ? Yes, ... but we are told, be not righteous overmuch ; and there are some virtues which dig their own graves."

He

He spoke in a disconnected manner; but his domestic misery was the string which threaded the different beads. Of West's interjected sympathy and well-meant efforts to turn his thoughts he took no heed.

"'Marriage is the metamorphosis of women.' Where did I read that lately? It's odd; but everything I now read relates to marriage. In every book I take up I find an emphatic warning against it. Why couldn't these have come in my way sooner? Why couldn't some one tell me?" Marriage is the metamorphosis of women—the Circe wand which changes back all these smiling, gentle, tractable, little girls into their true forms.

"Oh, but after all, you say? . . . . No, my wife does none of those things; but she has made my life miserable, miserable . . . . and that's enough for me. And if I were to try and explain how she does it, I daresay you would only laugh at me. For there's nothing tragic in the process. It's the thousand pin-pricks of daily life, the little oppositions, the little perversities, the faint sneers. At first you let them slip off again almost indifferently, but the slightest blow repeated upon the same place a thousand times draws blood at last.

"No, she doesn't care for me, and sometimes I almost think she hates the boy. Poor boy . . . . it seems monstrous, incredible; but I've caught her looking at him with a hardness, a coldness. . . . ."

He sat silent, looking wistfully away into space. West traced the beginning of a pleasanter train of ideas in the relaxed corners of his mouth, in the brightening of his sunken eyes.

"He's the dearest little chap, West! And so clever! Do you know, I believe he'll have the most extraordinarily logical and mathematical mind. He has begun to meditate already over what seems to him the arbitrariness of names. He wanted to know the
other

other day, for instance, how a table had come to be called a table, why it wasn't called a chair, or anything else you like. And this morning, when we were talking, he and I, over the present I had given him, he posed me this problem : Supposing two horses harnessed to a cart were galloping with it, just as fast as ever they could go, how much faster could ten horses gallop with it? Shows he thinks, eh ? Not bad for a child of four ? "

He began to forecast Cyril's career ; he would put his name down at Harrow, because to Harrow he could get out to see him every week. He should have the advantages of Oxford or Cambridge, which Catterson had not had. He should enter one of the liberal professions, the Bar for choice.

And then his face clouded over again.

" But he shall never marry. He shall do anything else in life he pleases : but he shall never marry. For it's no matter how well a man may be born, it's no matter how fortunate he may be in life, if he's unfortunate in his marriage. And it seems to me, that one way or another, marriage spells ruin."

He was back again in the unhappy present, and West felt his heart wrung. Yet there was no help to be given, no consolation possible. The one door of deliverance which stood open, was the one door which Catterson could not face, although his reluctant feet drew nearer to it every day.

But West had already observed that when life becomes impossible, when a man's strength is inadequate to the burdens imposed upon it, when the good he may yet accomplish is outweighed by the evils he may have to endure, then the door opens, the invisible hand beckons him through, and we know no further of his fate.

Though Catterson could not face it, and with an ominous spot burning on either cheek, tried to reabsorb himself again in plans for the future, West saw in it the only possible escape, and told
himself

himself it was better, even though it proved an eternal sleep, than
what he daily had to endure.

The wife's cold heart, her little cruelties, her little meannesses,
all her narrowness, her emptiness of mind rose before him. What
a hell upon earth to have to live in daily companionship with her,
even if unrelated to her in any way ! But for her husband she
was the constant living reminder of his dead illusions. He could
not look at her without seeing the poor, thin ghosts of his lost
youth, of his shattered faith, hope, and happiness, gathered round
her. Every indifference of hers, every neglect, must call up the
memory of some warm protestation, of some dear attention in the
past. And these were less hard to bear than the knowledge that
those had never been genuine.

It is life as you anticipated it, brought still fresh and palpitating
into contrast with the bleak reality, which is so intolerably hard to
bear.

The contemplation of Catterson's position became so painful to
West, that he felt he must get away even at the cost of
brutality. He gave warmly the asked for assurance to come
again soon, and knew in his heart as he uttered it, that he would
not soon find the courage to return.

In the hall he looked about him mechanically ; then let slip a
hot and vigorous word on discovering he had left his hat up in the
drawing-room and must go back.

The tea-table now stood by Nettie's elbow. She insisted that
he should take a cup of tea, pressing it on him as a sort of peace-
offering, so that without actual rudeness he could not refuse.
She was again gracious as far as she knew how to be. Possibly
Mrs. Reade, who studied the suavities of life, had been remonstrat-
ing with her.

Gladys lay on the hearthrug, her face in her hands, her elbows
planted

planted on the open book. The packet of sweets in a very knock-kneed and depleted condition stood beside her. She sucked a chocolate in her cheek, had kicked off her shoes, and drummed with her black-stockinged feet upon the floor.

West made a pretence of drinking his tea, but it was tepid, it was weak, and Nettie had put sugar into it without enquiring his tastes.

She and Mimi Reade were still discussing the patterns of the brocade.

"I do think the green perfectly sweet, Mimi," she repeated, holding the scrap up at arm's length, so that the lamplight might slant over it; "and yet the black is a softer, richer silk, and would make up awfully well with jet trimmings, as you say. I don't know which I had better have."

The two women turned and returned the problem, considered it again in all its bearings. They appeared to have forgotten West, which was but natural, he had sat silent for so long. To himself, his brain seemed mesmerised by the vapidity of their talk, so that an imbecile point of interest grew up within it, as to which colour, eventually, Nettie would choose.

Meanwhile the study door opened, and Catterson's cough, which carried such poignant suggestions to West, was heard again upon the stairs. It seemed to speak suggestively to Nettie too.

"After all," she said in her curious, drawling voice, "it would be more prudent I suppose to decide on the black."